AMINO ACID MOLECULES FRAGMENTATION BY LOW-ENERGY ELECTRONS

CHEMISTRY RESEARCH
AND APPLICATIONS

Additional books in this series can be found on Nova's website
under the Series tab.

Additional e-books in this series can be found on Nova's website
under the e-book tab.

CHEMISTRY RESEARCH AND APPLICATIONS

Amino Acid Molecules Fragmentation by Low-Energy Electrons

ALEXANDER V. SNEGURSKY,
JELENA TAMULIENE,
LIUDMILA G. ROMANOVA
AND VASYL S. VUKSTICH

New York

NOTICE TO THE READER

The Publisher has taken reasonable care in the preparation of this book, but makes no expressed or implied warranty of any kind and assumes no responsibility for any errors or omissions. No liability is assumed for incidental or consequential damages in connection with or arising out of information contained in this book. The Publisher shall not be liable for any special, consequential, or exemplary damages resulting, in whole or in part, from the readers' use of, or reliance upon, this material. Any parts of this book based on government reports are so indicated and copyright is claimed for those parts to the extent applicable to compilations of such works.

Independent verification should be sought for any data, advice or recommendations contained in this book. In addition, no responsibility is assumed by the publisher for any injury and/or damage to persons or property arising from any methods, products, instructions, ideas or otherwise contained in this publication.

This publication is designed to provide accurate and authoritative information with regard to the subject matter covered herein. It is sold with the clear understanding that the Publisher is not engaged in rendering legal or any other professional services. If legal or any other expert assistance is required, the services of a competent person should be sought. FROM A DECLARATION OF PARTICIPANTS JOINTLY ADOPTED BY A COMMITTEE OF THE AMERICAN BAR ASSOCIATION AND A COMMITTEE OF PUBLISHERS.

Additional color graphics may be available in the e-book version of this book.

Library of Congress Cataloging-in-Publication Data

ISBN: 978-1-63117-449-0

Published by Nova Science Publishers, Inc. † New York

CONTENTS

PREFACE

The present monograph is dedicated to the analysis of the most up-to date data on electron-impact induced fragmentation of a group of amino acid molecules that includes glycine, methionine and alanine. Such data are of a great importance because ionizing radiation causes in live tissue the irreversible effects at the genetic level. The mechanism of such degradation does not include the direct action of high-energy ionizing radiation only, because the influence of the processes related to the low-energy secondary electrons appear to be significant. Note that the primary radiation causes about one third of the mutagenic transformations in the cell, whereas most of the above radiation-induced transformations are related to the secondary electrons producing free radicals. Secondary products of ionizing radiation in living tissues are capable of damaging the structural units of nucleic acids and proteins leading, in particular, to dissociative ionization with both positive and negative-ion production. Thus, the low-energy electrons are of primary interest from the viewpoint of tracing the consequences of both malignant transformations in living cells under the influence of ionizing radiation and also provide useful radiation therapy effect on tumors in human beings. Present monograph would be useful for those students, post-graduates and scientists who work in the filed of studying the properties of amino acids and their practical applications in medicine, pharmaceutics, chemistry, atomic and molecular physics.

INTRODUCTION

Amino acids belong to biologically relevant organic substances involved in the live organisms. Generally, they include the amine (NH_2) and the carboxylic acid (COOL) functional groups. In general, their generic formula looks like $H_2NCHRCOOH$, here R being an organic substituent (a "side-chain"). As seen, their main constituents are carbon, hydrogen, oxygen and nitrogen atoms, however other elements (say, sulfur) are also found in their side-chains. As of today, a dozens of amino acids are known being classified quite differently. From the structural viewpoint and according to locations of their functional groups, amino acids are commonly classified as the α-, β-, γ- and δ- ones. Being involved in forming proteins, amino acids are the second (after water) largest component of live tissues. Together with proteins, they play a significant role in a number of live organism-related processes, e.g., neurotransmitter transport and biosynthesis [1].

Amino acids also serve as building blocks of proteins and intermediates in metabolism. The chemical properties of amino acids determine the biological activity of the proteins. The latter do not only catalyze most of the reactions in living cells, they also control all cellular processes. In addition, proteins contain the necessary information needed to determine the structure and the stability of the human body. This is an important field of scientific research, and today is still one of the most important tasks of modern biological and chemical science [2].

Generally, according to the most up-to date data, amino acids combine the 23 proteinogenic ("protein-building") substances involved into the peptide chains ("polypeptides"). All of them are the L-stereoisomers (the so-called "left-handed" isomers), while in bacteria and antibiotics a few D-amino acids (i.e., "right-handed" isomers) do occur. The 20 of the 23 proteinogenic amino acids are encoded directly by triplet codons in the genetic code and are usually called the "standard" amino acids.

Some of proteinogenic and non-proteinogenic amino acids also play the critical role in the live bodies. For instance, in the human brain, glutamate (standard glutamic acid) and the gamma-amino-butyric acid are, respectively, the principal neurotransmitters, whereas glycine is involved in synthesizing the porphyrins in red blood cells.

It is a known fact [3] that the 9 of the 20 standard amino acids are traditionally called the "essential" ones because they are not synthesized by the human body, and, thus, must be supplied in its diet. Please note that essential amino acids may also differ between different species. Respectively, other amino acids are called "non-essential" ones.

Due to their biological significance, amino acids are important in nutrition and are commonly used in nutritional supplements, fertilizers, and food technology. The field of their industrial use includes drugs manufacturing and production of numerous biodegradable plastics and chiral catalysts.

As mentioned above, amino acids, according to their side-chain, are usually classified into the four types. Regarding the standard α-amino acids, all of them, except for glycine, can exist in two enantiomers, called L or D amino acids being the mirror images of each other. While the L-amino acids represent all of the amino acids in proteins, the D-amino acids are found in some proteins produced by enzyme posttranslational modifications after translation and translocation to the endoplasmic reticulum. These substances serve as the components of the peptidoglycan cell walls of bacteria, while D-serine is known as the neurotransmitter in the human brain. The L and D amino acids do not take part in the optical activity of the live tissue, they are rather related to the optical activity of the isomer of glyceraldehyde from which that amino acid can be synthesized.

Amino acids as the structural units of proteins produce the polymer chains (i.e., peptides) or longer chains called either polypeptides or proteins. These polymers are linear and unbranched, with each amino acid within the chain being attached to the two neighboring amino acids. Such process of protein formation is called translation and involves the step-by-step addition of amino acids to a growing protein chain by a ribozyme called a ribosome. The order in which the amino acids are added is determined by the genetic code from an mRNA template, which is a RNA copy of one of the organism's genes.

The non-standard amino acids found in proteins are formed by post-translational modifications. These modifications are essential in proteins, e.g., carboxylation of glutamate favors binding of calcium cations, and hydroxylation of proline is critical for maintaining connective tissues. Another example is the formation of hypusine in the translation initiation factor EIF5A through modification of a lysine residue. Such modifications can also determine the localization of the protein, e.g., the addition of long hydrophobic groups can cause a protein to bind to a phospholipid membrane.

The 20 standard amino acids are used to synthesize proteins and other biomolecules or are oxidized to urea and carbon dioxide as a source of energy. The oxidation pathway includes the removal of the amino group by a transaminase, and then the amino group is involved into the urea cycle. The other product of transamidation is a keto acid that enters the citric acid cycle. Glucogenic amino acids can also be converted into glucose due to the gluconeogenesis process.

Regarding the possible degradation of amino acids under the external impact, it is known that ionizing radiation causes in live tissue the irreversible effects at the genetic level [4]. The mechanism of such degradation does not include the direct action of high-energy ionizing radiation only, because the influence of the processes related to the low-energy secondary electrons appear to be significant [5]. Note that the primary radiation causes about one third of the mutagenic transformations in the cell [5], whereas most of the above radiation-induced transformations are related to the secondary electrons producing free radicals. Secondary products of ionizing radiation in living tissues are capable of damaging the structural units of nucleic acids and proteins leading, in particular, to dissociative ionization with both positive and negative-ion production. Thus, the low-energy electrons are of primary interest from the viewpoint of tracing the consequences of both malignant transformations in living cells under the influence of ionizing radiation and also provide useful radiation therapy effect on tumors in human beings [6].

This specifies a particular interest in studying inelastic processes of slow-electron interactions with biological molecules. They include, in particular, the electron-impact excitation, electron attachment (including dissociative one) as well as direct and dissociative ionization. Dissociative ionization is extremely important due to the production of the parent molecule fragments both in the ionized and neutral states. Among a wide variety of the above targets amino acids are peculiar not only due to the fact that they are the building blocks of the human body (see above) but also in view of the role they could have played in the genesis and development of the life on the Earth. Current research has shown the presence of amino acids in various space objects (say, comets and meteorites) that, in principle, may prove the idea of the external 'life import' to our planet [7].

The studies of the basic mechanisms of the amino acid molecule structural changes caused by low-energy electron impact are far from being complete or consistent despite their undoubted significance. According to the National Institute of Standards (NIST) database [8], the available relevant data are a bit disputable and controversial, while those on the parent molecule ionization thresholds and fragment appearance energies are extremely scarce.

In this book, we present the systemized data on the electron-impact fragmentation of some amino acid molecules, namely, glycine, methionine and alanine, having different organic substituents R: $-H$, $-CH_3$ and $-C_2H_4SCH_3$. One of them involves not only the main constituents such as carbon and hydrogen, but the sulfur atom as well. Moreover, the electronegativity of the above substituents is different. Thus, the above amino acids are very good examples to predict the influence of substituents on the process of fragmentation of the core part ($H_2NCHCOOH$) of the amino acid. This information is based on our up-to-date results on studying the processes occurring in these molecules and will be generalized below with subsequent reference made to our previous papers.

Chapter 1

EXPERIMENTAL

In our study, we used a conventional magnetic mass-spectrometer MI-1201 [9] as the mass-separator unit enabling the fragments of electron-molecule interaction to be identified. Figure 1 shows the schematic diagram of the experimental setup. The experimental apparatus developed and applied is based, as already mentioned above, on the magnetic mass spectrometer capable of operating within the 1–720 a.m.u. mass range. High sensitivity ($\sim 10^{-16}$ A) and resolution (± 0.25 a.m.u.) of the mass analyzer enabled the fragments of the target molecule to be reliably separated and detected even at low levels of ion currents reaching the ion detector.

The primary molecular beam (M in Figure 1) was formed by means of an effusion source with a resistive oven providing target molecule concentrations not less than 10^{10} molecule/cm^3. The operating temperature of the molecular beam source was varied up to 200°C being controlled by a thermocouple allowing the temperature dependences of the fragment yields to be determined. The temperature and pressure conditions of the molecular beam formation excluded the possibility of molecular cluster formation. A specially designed three-electrode electron gun provided an electron current I_e=30–50 μA over a wide (0–150 eV) energy range. This source enabled the energy dependences of ionization and dissociative ionization cross sections to be measured in the incident electron energy range from the threshold up to 150 eV. The ions M^+ produced in the ion source and extracted by the electric field entered a magnetic ion separator and were detected by means of an electrometer.

The data acquisition and processing system was controlled by a PC. Special measures were taken to stabilize the mass analyzer transmission thus making the mass of the fragment under study to be reliably fixed. An electron energy scale was calibrated with respect to known ionization thresholds for argon atom and nitrogen molecule (see below) with the accuracy not worse than ±0.1 eV.

The molecular beam M (see Figure 1) was directed to the ionization chamber perpendicularly to the electron beam (the beams intersect in the plane of the figure). The experimental procedure was as follows. First both electron and molecular beam sources were put into operation and after reaching the optimal conditions of beam generation a mass spectrum of the molecules under study was measured. Since the amino acid molecules may undergo strong thermal decomposition, the above mass spectra were measured serially at different molecular beam source oven temperatures. As an example, the temperature dependence of production of the ionized fragment with $m=30$ a.m.u. (here m being the mass of the fragment) from the methionine molecule measured at the 66 eV ionization energy is shown in Figure 2. Analyzing these data, one may conclude that the temperature range of up to $120^{\circ}C$ appears to be optimal to obtain a stable beam of all the molecules under study providing reliable detection of the signal at the ion detector and ensuring no essential effect of thermal degradation. This is confirmed by the data on the thermogravimetric studies of L-α amino acids [10].

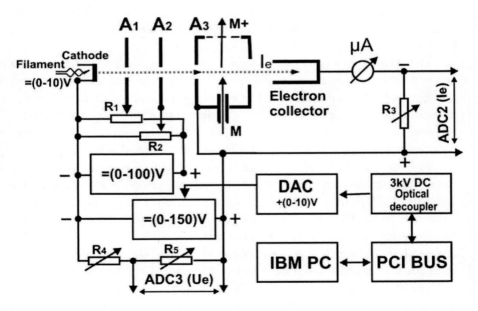

Figure 1. Schematic diagram of the experimental setup and supporting electrical circuits.

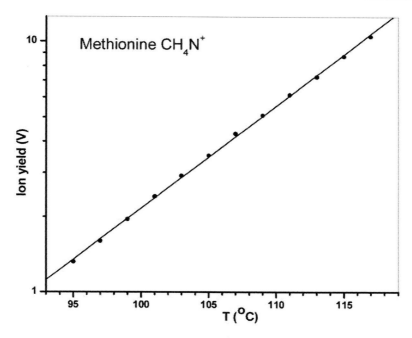

Figure 2. Temperature dependence of the CH_4N^+ ion yield from the methionine molecule.

The masses of the fragments produced were then fixed and the energy dependences of the relevant ion yields were measured. Electron energy was varied with an energy step of 0.1–0.3 eV enabling the threshold areas of the dissociative ionization functions for all the fragments under study to be measured. In this case the problem of the incident electron energy scale calibration becomes very significant. To calibrate the above energy scale we have measured first the threshold areas of the ionization functions for the two test gases – Ar and N_2. The experimental ionization thresholds were determined by means of a fitting technique suggested by T. Maerk's group (see, e.g., our earlier paper [11]). This technique is based on a least-square method approximation using the Marquardt-Levenberg algorithm. The details of this method can be found elsewhere (see, e.g., [12]). The threshold areas of the energy dependences of the ionization cross-sections for Ar and N_2 are shown in Figures 3a and 3b, respectively. For comparison, Figure 3a also shows the data on the Ar^+ ion production measured by Freund et al. [13]. One may note that the fitted curves have sharper thresholds as compared to the initial experimental ones. This is mainly due to the fact that the above fitting procedure does not take into account possible contributions of the excited ionic states lying just above the ionization threshold (note that fitting is carried out in a certain incident electron energy range that covers excitation thresholds for such states). However, this does not influence substantially the results obtained in this work.

As seen, our data agree well with the Freund's results within the limits of the experimental uncertainty confirming the reliability of the fitting technique applied in this work. The absolute value of the Ar atom ionization threshold energy obtained by us (E=15.76 eV) agrees accurately with that known and included into a number of databases (see, e.g., the NIST database [8]). The same is valid for the data obtained here for the nitrogen molecule (see Figure 3b). The ionization threshold value for this molecule determined by us (15.56 eV) agrees extremely well with the NIST data [8]. Thus, our technique, obviously, ensured reliable measuring the absolute energy thresholds for the processes under study.

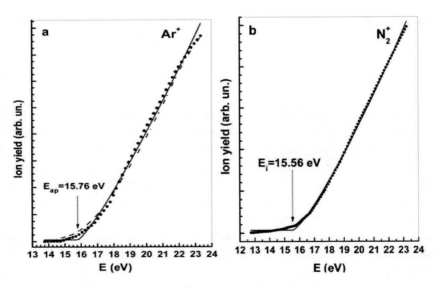

Figure 3. Near-threshold areas of the energy dependences of the ionization cross-sections for the Ar atom (a) and N_2 molecule (b). Solid circles – present experiment. Solid lines – our data fitted using the least-square technique. Dashed line – data of Freund et al. [13]. Arrows indicate the ionization threshold values obtained using the fitting procedure.

Chapter 2

THEORETICAL

In this section, we will shortly describe the theoretical approach used in the present study. The structure of the molecules and their fragments have been studied by using the generalized gradient approximation for the exchange-correlation potential in the density functional theory (DFT) as it is described by the Becke's three-parameter hybrid functional, applying the non-local correlation provided by Lee, Yang, and Parr. The DFT method is commonly referred to as B3LYP [14], i.e., as a representative standard DFT method described in more detail below. The cc-pVTZ basis set has been used as well [15]. The structures of the molecule isomers/conformers and their fragments under study have been optimized globally without any symmetry constraint. The bond order and the bond length of the molecule conformers have been investigated to find the weaker bonds possible to be destructed. Additionally, the vibration spectrum has been evaluated to predict the possible elongation of bonds and the change of the angle aiming to analyze the most probable fragments produced due to electron impact. On the other hand, the results on the vibration modes have been analyzed to be sure that the equilibrium point of the molecular systems is found. In order to model the fragmentation processes, the possible fragment anions, cations and fragments with a zero charge have been evaluated. Dissociation energies were calculated as the difference between the total energy of the molecule and the sum of the energies of the fragments predicted. We have assumed that in our experimental conditions the structure of the fragments formed could be changed, influencing, thus, the dissociation energy. To evaluate the above influence, the dissociation energy has been calculated for the following two cases: i) the single point energy calculation of the fragments was performed taking into account the geometry of a certain part of the molecules under study (in these cases the energy of fragment formation is not the lowest one); ii) the structure of the fragments has been optimized, i.e., the fragments were allowed to reach their equilibrium geometry and the obtained energy (the lowest energy of the fragments) was used to calculate the dissociation energy.

2.1. Wave Functions and Basis Sets

In the quantum-chemical calculations, the wave functions of the system are composed as the linear combinations of elementary functions called the basis orbitals [16]. The mathematical approach adapted to describe both atoms and molecules is presented below.

Any function may be composed as a linear combination of elementary functions:

$$f(x) = c_1\phi_1(x) + c_2\phi_2(x) + c_3\phi_3(x) + \cdots,$$

(1)

where x is a variable.

Using the composition of equation (1), the completeness of the basis set is to be described.

If one assumes that the variable x is referred to the interval $[a, b]$, the functions $f(x)$ under study as well as the functions $\phi_1(x), \phi_2(x), \phi_3(x)$ ...will be defined in this interval. Then the function $f(x)$ may be approximated as follows:

$$f(x) = c_1\phi_1(x) + c_2\phi_2(x) + c_3\phi_3(x) + \cdots + c_n\phi_n,$$

(2)

where a finite number of basis orbitals is included.

The composition coefficients are chosen in such a way that the integral

$$D = \int_a^b (f(x) - f_n(x))^2 dx$$

has a minimal value, thus, such composition is the most accurate one. This approximation is the most accurate when ortonormalized functions are applied. In this case, the composition coefficients are equal to [17]:

$$c_i = \langle \phi_i(x) | f(x) \rangle.$$

(3)

When $D \to 0$ for every function $f(x)$ defined in the interval $[a, b]$, the set of functions is complete. Then the function $f(x)$ takes the form:

$$f(x) = \sum_{i=1} c_i \phi_i(x).$$

(4)

In the case when the function has two variables, and the set $\{\phi_i(x_i)\}*$ is complete for x_1 in the interval $[a, b]$, as well as $\{\phi_i'(x_i)\}*$ is complete for x_2 in the interval $[a', b']$, the function $f(x)$ of the system is:

$$f(x) = \sum_{i,j} c_{i,j} \phi_i(x_1) \phi_j(x_2).$$

(5)

The above-mentioned bilinear combination is valid if the coefficients c_i are:

$$c_i = c_{i1} \varphi_1'(x_2) + c_{i2} \varphi_2'(x_3).$$

(6)

The similar bilinear combination for the multi-variable function is constructed in the same way and the above-mentioned functions take the form [17]:

$$\varphi(r_1, r_2, r_3, \dots r_n) = \sum c_{i,j,k,\dots p} \phi_i(r_1) \phi_j(r_2) \dots \phi_p(r_p).$$

Subscripts $i, j, \dots p$ denote the orbitals from the complete set of orbitals . $\phi_1, \phi_2, \phi_3, \dots \phi_p$. The above mathematical wave functional approaches are valid for any quantum system of many identical particles. However, new features were observed.

When investigating many-electron systems, additional conditions are important for the wave functions, i.e., the wave functions of the system should be antisymmetrized with respect to permutations of coordinates. The antisymmetric functions are of the form:

$$\varphi(r_1, r_2, r_3, \dots r_n = \sum_{i,j,k,\dots p} c_{i,j,k,\dots p} \Phi_{i,j,k,\dots p}(r_1, r_2, r_3, \dots r_n)$$

(7)

where $\Phi_{i,j,k,\ldots p}(r_1, r_2, r_3, \ldots r_n) = M_{i,j,k,\ldots p} \sum_p \varepsilon_p \hat{P} \, \varphi_A(r_1)\varphi_B(r_2) \ldots \varphi_x(r_n)$ and $\hat{P}$ is a permutation operator; ε_p is equal to 1 or -1 dependent of the parity $\hat{P}$; M_x is the normalization constant.

The sum shown in Eq. (7) may be written in the following form:

$$\Phi_{i,j,k,\ldots p}(r_1, r_2, r_3, \ldots r_n) = M_{i,j,k,\ldots p} \det |\phi_A(r_1)\phi_B(r_2) \ldots \phi_x(r_n)|.$$

(8)

For convenience, only diagonal elements of the determinant are indicated.

In the quantum chemical calculations, the linear combinations of atomic functions are used to approximate the molecular orbitals. The use of these combinations implies that the identity of an atom is not destroyed, but perturbed slightly only. These combinations are applied, because finding one-electron wave functions for the molecules is a more complicated problem than that for the atoms. The nuclear potential in the atom is of a spherically symmetrical form and, therefore, it is possible to separate the radial, angular and spin parts of the wave function. On the other hand, the molecules are the many-center systems, and such separation of variables is impossible. Therefore, practically it is very difficult to calculate an integral over the three variables.

To make the above-mentioned solution easier the molecular orbitals are expressed as the linear combinations of atomic functions (see (4)). This approximation is called the linear combination of atomic orbitals (LCAO). Such an approximation is based on two assumptions. First, it is assumed that the potential of an electron localized near to a nucleus in a molecule is completely described by the potential of this nucleus, and the potentials of other atoms have a relatively small influence, therefore, they may be neglected. Second, the sets of molecular orbitals must continuously transit to the atomic orbital sets. This approximation describes the quantum states of molecules fairly well. However, the deficiency of accuracy appears due to incompleteness of the sets of basis functions when applying the above-mentioned method.

The wave functions contain much more detailed information than is actually needed in any practical application. It would be a very great computational simplification if calculating these extra insignificant things could be avoided. Below we consider more general way of describing the quantum states.

Assume that the one-electron system is studied. The single electron occupies the orbital A and its spin is equal to 1/2. The electron wave function coincides with $\phi_A(r)$, while the respective density function is $\rho = |\phi_A(r)|^2$.

This function describes the probability of finding the electron in the space dr. One-electron functions are used as the prototypes of the many-electron system functions. Thus, the above approach may be adopted for a many-electron system and the one-electron density matrix is used instead of the wave function in the form described in [18]:

$$\rho(r, r) = N \int \varphi^*(r_1, r_2, r_3, \ldots r_n)\varphi(r_1', r_2', r_3', \ldots r_n')dr_2 dr_3 \ldots dr_n, \tag{9}$$

where N is the number of electrons.

Similarly, the two-electron density matrix is defined as follows:

$$\rho(r_1, r_2, r_1', r_2') =$$
$$N\frac{(N-1)}{2}\int \varphi^*(r_1, r_2, r_3, \ldots r_n) \, \varphi(r_1', r_2', r_3', \ldots r_n')dr_3 dr_4 \ldots dr_N, \tag{10}$$

where $N\frac{(N-1)}{2}$ is the number of electron pairs.

When r coincides with r', the $\varphi^*(r_1, r_2, r_3, \ldots r_n)\varphi(r_1', r_2', r_3', \ldots r_n')$ part of (9) describes the probability of finding the first electron in the space dr_1 at the point r_1, the second electron in dr_2 at the point r_2, etc. The same result is obtained for any electron pair i, j when r_1 and r_2 coincide with r_1' and r_2', respectively; being the probability of finding two electrons in the points dr_1 and dr_2 at the same time, what is referred to as a pair density. One or two electron densities in the coordination space are most commonly applied:

$$\rho_1(r_1) = \rho_1(r_1, r_1); \quad \rho_2(r_1, r_2) = \rho_1(r_1, r_2, r_1, r_2). \tag{11}$$

The density functions (10) allow us to relate the averaged values of operators with electrons. Function (9) can be written as a bilinear combination of the basis orbitals [3]:

$$\rho_1(r_1, r_1') = \sum \rho_{1RS}\varphi_R(r)\varphi_S^*(r'), \tag{11a}$$

where is ρ_{1RS} a numerical coefficient, and the subscripts R, S denote orbitals.

If this bilinear form is derived from a single determinant, ρ_{1RR} is equal to 1 for the occupied orbitals and ρ_{1RS} is equal to 0 for the vacant ones. $\rho(r, r')$ is then considered diagonal because all the numerical coefficients are equal to 0 for any $R \neq S$.

The two- electron density matrix corresponding to a one-determinant wave function can be written in terms of one-electron density matrices:

$$\rho(r_1, r_2, r_1', r_2') =$$
$$\sum (\varphi_R(r_1)\varphi_S(r_2)\varphi_R^*(r_1')\varphi_S^*(r_2') - (\varphi_R(r_2)\varphi_S(r_1)\varphi_R^*(r_1')\varphi_S^*(r_2').$$

(12)

This implies that the two-electron density matrix is obtainable from the one-electron density matrices.

These approaches were constructed as the ways of calculating the electron density $\rho(r)$ or the many-electron wave functions $\Phi(r_1, r_2, ... r_n)$. The electron density of the ground state determines uniquely the external potential $V_{ext}(r)$ (the external potential is the external field in which the electrons move; while the external field is the electrostatic potential generated by the nuclei, the position and the spatial extension of which is assumed as fixed and negligible) [19]. The surrounding medium potential could also be taken into consideration. This implies that electron density in the three dimensional space is sufficient for constructing the total Hamiltonian operator when solving the Schrödinger equation. As a result, any ground state properties are obtained. Thus, the function determines any ground state property or any ground state property may be defined as a functional with respect to $\rho(r)$. The fixed linear combinations of atomic functions are called the basis sets. However, instead of having to calculate the mathematical form of the molecular orbitals (MO) (that is impossible using a computer), the problem is reduced to determining the MO expansion coefficients in terms of the basis functions of Slater or Gaussian types. The function is called a primitive function, or a primitive. The main disadvantage of the various basis set like contracted Gaussian functions is a large number of primitive functions required, because the number of computer integrals is proportional to the fourth power of the number of primitives. However, the two primary and competing criteria for selecting a basis set are the accuracy and size, i.e., a given set should be suitable to describe the system under study and computations should be performable. Thus, in our calculation, we used a contracted basis set, i.e., a smaller basis set that takes into account correlation effects with a ($12s6p$) primitive basis set contracted under the Raffenetti pathway and optimized at the Hartree-Fock (HF) level; the configuration interaction calculation with single and double excitations from all the degenerate HF configurations has been performed as well [19, 20].

As example, the correlation consistent polarized valence basis sets (cc-pYXZ, where X corresponds to D or T) could be considered as the compact sets of primitive Gaussian functions. The (sp) sets can be obtained from the atomic HF calculations, while the polarization (d, f, g, ...) sets must be determined from the correlated atomic calculations. Adding a set of primitive (spd) functions to the atomic HF orbitals forms the double-zeta (cc-pVDZ) basis set. The exponents for the correlation functions follow from correlated calculations on atoms, specifically for HF plus single and double excited wave functions. For the final sets, the (sp) correlation functions were obtained by uncontracting the most diffused s and p functions from an appropriate HF set, since these functions are demonstrated as being close to the optimal s and d functions. The triple-zeta (cc-pVTZ) basis is obtained by adding the sets of the (2d1f) polarization functions plus those of uncontracted (2s2p) primitives from the appropriate HF(sp) sets to the atomic HF orbitals.

These basis sets show an excellent behavior in calculating both atoms and molecules. In fact, cc-pVDZ achieves 99% of the correlation energy obtained with the ANO basis sets, although the latter have almost double number of primitives.

2.2. Density Functional Theory Approach

The density functional theory allows one to replace both the complicated many-electron wave functions and the respected Schrödinger equation by a much simpler electron density functions and by a new calculation way. The above- mentioned replacement is based on the Hohenberg-Kohn theorem [21].

Consequently, the electron density also determines the ground-state wave function and all other electronic properties of the system, for example, the kinetic energy $T[\rho]$, the potential energy $V[\rho]$ and the total energy $E[\rho]$. Thus, on the basis of the above-mentioned theorem, a more general expression, which can include terms taking into account both the exchange energy and the electron correlation, is applied.

The first step in this direction leads to the Thomas-Fermi theory and its improvements. Statistical approach is applied in which it is assumed that the number of electrons, as well as the density itself, is so large that the average quantities are accurate.

First, the space containing N electrons is divided into many small cells having a side l. The volume of the one cell is l^3. Each cell contains a fixed number of electrons that is different for different cells. It is assumed that these electrons behave themselves like independent fermions with the cells independent of each other. The total energy of electrons in this cell is found by summing up the contributions of different energy states [22]:

$$\Delta E = \frac{8\,\pi}{5}\left(\frac{2m}{h^2}\right)^{3/2} l^3\,\varepsilon_F^{5/2}\,,\tag{13}$$

where m ε_F is the so-called Fermi energy that is the zero-temperature limit of the chemical potential.

The number of electrons in the cube is as follows [23]:

$$\Delta N = \frac{8\,\pi}{3}\left(\frac{2m}{h^2}\right)^{3/2} l^3\,\varepsilon_F^{3/2}\,.\tag{14}$$

Eliminating ε_F from (14) and using (13), one obtains [21]:

$$\Delta E = \frac{3}{5}\,\Delta N\,\varepsilon = \frac{3h^2}{10m}\left(\frac{3}{8\,\pi}\right)^{2/3} l^3\left(\frac{\Delta N}{l^3}\right)^{5/3}\,.\tag{15}$$

This equation is the relation between the total kinetic energy and the electron density

$$\rho(r) = \frac{\Delta N}{l^3}$$

for each cell in the space. Adding the contribution from all cells, we obtain the total kinetic energy reverted to atomic units:

$$T[\rho] = 2.871 \int \rho^{5/3}(r)dr,\tag{16}$$

where the limit $l^3 \rightarrow 0$ was taken to replace summation by integration. This is the famous Thomas-Fermi kinetic energy functional, which Thomas and Fermi dared to apply to electrons in atoms. Further, the energy related to the external potential can be written in the form [22]:

$$V_e[\rho] = Z \int \frac{\rho(r)}{r} dr \qquad (17)$$

and the classical electrostatic Coulomb energy is:

$$V[\rho] = \frac{1}{2} \int \rho(r) V_c(r) dr \;, \qquad (18)$$

where V_c is the potential energy of electrons.

Then the total energy of many-electron system is equal to [21]:

$$E[\rho] = 2.71 \int \rho^{5/3} dr - Z \int \frac{\rho(r)}{r} dr + \iint \frac{\rho(r_1)\rho(r_2)}{|r_1 - r_2|} dr_1 dr_2. \qquad (19)$$

When the energy dependence of the external potential is explicit, equation (19) takes the form:

$$E[\rho] = T[\rho] + \int \rho(r)(V_{ext} + \frac{1}{2} V_c(r) dr + E_{xc}[\rho], \qquad (20)$$

where $E_{xc} = \int \varepsilon_{xc}(\rho)\rho(r) dr$ is the exchange-correlation energy functional, and ε_{xc} is the electron density function. Therefore, the full n-body wave function is not required as only the total electron density calculations are to be performed in order to obtain all the ground-state properties. Equation (20) cannot be solved explicitly for $N>2$. Therefore various approximations are used for its solution.

Different non-local or local approximations (also called the generalized gradient approximations) of the density functional are used, because no general exact functional exists. The non-local approximations differ from the local ones in the dependence of the first- and second-order derivatives of $\rho(r)$, i.e., the non-local functional is improved over the local one by being functions not only of $\rho(r)$, but also of $|\nabla\rho(r)|$ and $|\nabla^2\rho(r)|$. The non-local approximations, unlike HF one, include explicitly no dependence on the long-range behavior of $\rho(r)$. Therefore, combination of both HF and DFT methods allows hybrid methods to be constructed. The hybrid methods include a mixture of the HF exchange with the DFT exchange-correlation. One of these methods is described by the Becke's three-parameter hybrid functional, applying the non-local correlation provided by Lee, Yang, and Parr. The DFT method is commonly referred to as B3LYP, i.e., a representative standard DFT method. The widely used gradient-corrected exchange energy functional is that published by Becke in the form:

$$\Delta E_x = -\beta \int \rho(r)^{4/3} \frac{x_\sigma^2}{1+6x_\sigma sinh^{-1}x_\sigma}, \tag{21}$$

where β is an easily determined parameter with the least-square satisfying the exact atomic HF data and

$$x_\sigma = \frac{|\rho_\sigma(r)|}{\rho_\sigma^{4/3}}. \tag{22}$$

At the same time the Lee, Yang, Parr gradient-corrected correlation may be used. In this case the correlation energy is calculated by the following formula [24]:

$$E_c = -a \int \frac{\rho(r)+b\rho(r)^{-2/3}[t_{HF}(r)-2t_w(r)e^{-c\rho(r)^{-1/3}}}{1+d\rho(r)^{-1/3}}, \tag{23}$$

where

$t_w(r) = \frac{1}{8}\left(\frac{|\nabla\rho(r)|^2}{\rho(r)} - \nabla^2\rho(r)\right)$ is the Weirsacher kinetic energy density,

whereas $t_{HF}(r) = \frac{1}{8}\sum\frac{|\rho_i(r)|^2}{\rho_i(r)} - \nabla^2\rho(r)$ is the Hartree Fock kinetic energy density.

The density functional methods are derived for obtaining total energies, for examples, such as the functional of the structure. Thus, despite of problems and limitations, the currently applied DFT models are capable of providing very useful information, which otherwise can be obtained often only whit great difficulty when other experimental or theoretical methods are applied. The present DFT models are the ones for calculating total energies as the function of the nuclear position and are very suitable for the appearance energy calculations (see below).

Chapter 3

RESULTS AND DISCUSSION

3.1. Glycine

The experimental mass-spectrum of glycine is shown in Figure 4.

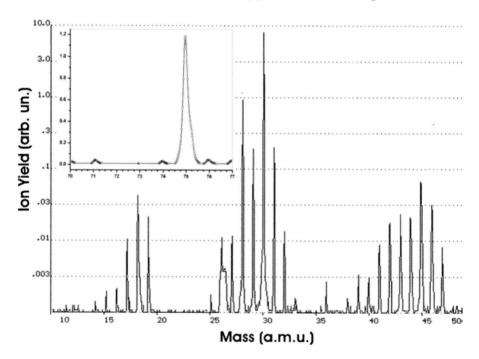

Figure 4. Mass spectrum of the glycine molecule. Inset – that in the vicinity of the parent peak.

As seen, the fragments observed are due to the process of electron-impact dissociative ionization of the molecule under study. It is a very peculiar feature of the above mass-spectrum that the parent ion peak (see inset in Figure 4) is rather weak allowing one to conclude that its formation is less probable because of its decay within a short period of the collision time. This pattern is typical for a number of complex molecules not comprising conjugated bonds [25]. Nevertheless, we may state, that, despite the weak intensity of the parent molecular ion peak, dissociative ionization of the initial molecule provides a rich spectrum of the ionized fragments.

The most prominent peak in the mass-spectrum (Figure 4) is due to formation of the parent molecule fragment with the $m=30$ a.m.u. mass. Probable assignments of this peak are the CH_4N^+ and CH_2O^+ ions. As we have found earlier [26], the first fragment may involve two isomers: $NH_2CH_2^+$ and CH_3NH^+. Formation of the CH_3NH^+ fragment is less probable because of its thermodynamical instability [26, 27]. Regarding the CH_2O^+ fragment, its formation is related to the substantial energy consumption for the rearrangement of atoms and bonds in the parent molecular ion. Thus, this process is less probable as compared to that for the above CH_4N^+ fragment. Formation of the most intense ion fragment with the $m=30$ a.m.u. mass, i.e., the CH_4N^+ ion, should result from the 'amine type' ionization of the parent $C_2H_5NO_2$ molecule and the bond rupture at the adjacent carbon atom with the subsequent loss of the neutral CHO_2 radical.

The next (by its intensity) peak in the mass spectrum (at $m=28$ a.m.u.) is related to formation of the CH_2N^+ ion fragment. As it is obvious from [26], the main component of this peak is due to the $HCNH^+$ isomer formation. The next fragment with the $m=29$ a.m.u. mass should be assigned to the CH_3N^+ ion.

Figure 5 presents the area of the mass-spectrum of the glycine molecule under study in the mass region from 27.5 to 30.5 a.m.u. The most interesting, in our opinion, is a weak peak located at $m=28.5$ a.m.u. To our knowledge, we were the first to observe it experimentally. Below we shall proceed with the analysis of the mechanisms of the above fragments production. Note that in Figure 4 it is not revealed so clearly as in Figure 5 due to the semi-logarithmic scale used.

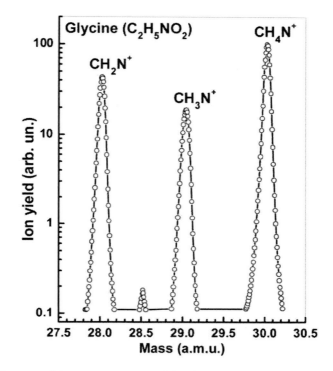

Figure 5. The area of the mass-spectrum of the glycine molecule showing the doubly charged CH_2NHCO^{2+} fragment production.

First, the bond length and the bond order of the neutral glycine molecule were analyzed to determine its most probable fragmentation channels under the ionizing radiation influence (see Table 1).

Table 1. The glycine molecule bond lengths and orders

Bonds	Bond length, (Å)	Bond order
C1 – C2	1.52	0.85
C1 – N4	1.46	0.98
C1 – H8	1.09	0.94
C1 – H10	1.09	0.94
C2 – O3	1.38	1.01
C2 – O5	1.23	1.98
O3 – H9	0.98	0.80
N4 – H7	1.01	0.87

The molecule image and the atom numbers are presented in Figure 6.

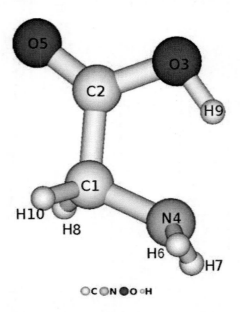

Figure 6. The general view of the glycine molecule investigated.

It is seen that the O3–H9 bond is the weakest one. So, the $C_2H_4NO_2^-$ fragment could be formed due to deprotonation of the glycine molecule and this process is described in detail in [28]. We had no possibility to investigate anions experimentally, thus the main task of this study was to describe the fragmentation process that leads to the appearance of positively charged fragments, therefore formation of the $C_2H_4NO_2^-$ fragment is not described here in detail.

The second weakest bond is that between the carbon atoms. Based on these results and using the Mulliken and Lowdin population analysis, one may predict that the CH_4N and CHO_2 fragments should be produced via the glycine molecule dissociation.

According to the early (that has become classical) work [29], this fragmentation process is related to the removal of one electron from the nitrogen lone pair resulting in the charge localization on the nitrogen atom and on the adjacent α-carbon atom. Such 'amine type' ionization seems to dominate over other possible ionization channels, hence the simplest analysis of the bond order and allows us to predict the most probable fragmentation processes occurring at the C–C bond break. The relevant processes could be as follows:

$$C_2H_5NO_2 + e \rightarrow \begin{cases} CHO_2^- + CH_4N^+ + e; & (24) \\ CHO_2^0 + CH_4N^+ + 2e; & (25) \\ CHO_2^+ + CH_4N^- + e; & (26) \\ CHO_2^+ + CH_4N^0 + 2e; & (27) \\ CHO_2^+ + CH_4N^+ + 3e. & (28) \end{cases}$$

Calculated appearance energies for the above fragments are listed in Table 2. The appearance energy E_{ap} was calculated as: $E_{ap} = E_{glycine} - (E_{CHO2} + E_{CH4N})$. Here $E_{glycine}$ is the total energy of the neutral glycine molecule, while E_{CHO2} and E_{CH4N} are those of the CHO_2 and CH_4N fragments, respectively. This calculation does not take into account the activation energy of the molecular ion fragmentation. One may notice that the lowest energy is required to divide the glycine molecule into the CHO_2^- anion and the CH_4N^+ cation (see pathway (24)).

Table 2. Calculated appearance energies (in eV)
for the CHO_2 and CH_4N fragments

CHO_2 ($m=45$ a.m.u.) charge	CH_4N ($m=30$ a.m.u.) charge	Glycine molecule geometry not changed*	Glycine molecule geometry changed**
-1	1	10.6	8.57
0	1	12.03	9.99
1	-1	16.62	16.11
1	0	15.26	14.99
1	1	23.17	21.14

*' Glycine molecule geometry not changed' means that the single point energy calculation of the fragments taking into account the geometry of the certain part of the glycine molecule was performed.

**' Glycine molecule geometry changed' indicates that the equilibrium geometry structure of the glycine molecule fragments is investigated.

The positive CH_4N^+ ion is produced according to pathway (25) with higher energy consumption if it is predicted that only the C–C bond of the glycine molecule is ruptured, i.e., the bond length and angles in the parent molecule and their fragments are the same. Additionally, we have observed a slight shoulder in the ionization function for this fragment [26], which, in our opinion, results from the contribution of a new channel of the parent molecule dissociation. This should be related both to the second ionization energy of the parent molecule and to the change of the fragment charge.

According to our measurements, the appearance energy for the CH_4N^+ fragment is 10.1 ± 0.1 eV, which is close to the calculated value (9.99 eV) for the molecule conformer under study in case of dissociation of the glycine molecule geometry with fragment change according to pathway (25). Taking into account the different glycine molecule conformers in the ion source of the mass-spectrometer are in the dynamical equilibrium and that the difference of their total energies is about 0.1 eV [30], one may conclude that the main dissociative channel of the parent ion with the CH_4N^+ ion production proceeds according to pathway (25). It should be noted that, according to the photoionization data [31], the appearance energy for this ion is 9.38 ± 0.05 eV. Higher ionization energy and appearance energy values for electron impact as compared to photoionization are explained usually by the influence of spin polarization and Coulomb interaction both before and after collision. For example, spin polarization reduces the ionization energy of glycine by about 0.24 eV [32]. Therefore, in the case of glycine photoionization, one has to take into account process (24) as well, leading to the ion pair formation, which is more probable as compared to other possible processes described above.

The main fragment peak CH_4N^+ ($m=30$ a.m.u.) in the glycine molecule mass spectrum is accompanied by the satellite peaks with $m=28$, 29 and 31 a.m.u., which correspond to the ionic fragments produced due to either the hydrogen atom migration/detachment or to the main fragment dehydration. The relative intensity of the peak at $m=31$ a.m.u. in our mass-spectrum is about 1.8–5.5% of the CH_4N^+ ion peak depending on the ionization conditions. The calculated height of the first isotope peak for this ion as the sum of the increments of the relative intensities for the atomic isotopes is 1.55% and this testifies to the fact that the observed peak is a compound one and comprises the $^{13}CH_4N^+$ and CH_5N^+ ions. Presumably, the CH_5N^+ ion contribution to the total peak intensity is dependent of the migration rate of the H atom from the hydroxyl group, and in our experiment it is considerably higher than that in the relevant NIST database [8]. Most probably, the structure of the CH_5N^+ ion is related to that of methylamine, i.e., the $CH_3NH_2^+$ ion.

For the $CH_3NH_2^+$ ion, the complementary fragment corresponds to the neutral CO_2 particle. In the glycine mass spectrum, the relative intensity of the peak at $m=44$ a.m.u. (i.e., the CO_2^+ ion) is 5.8 % [8]. This pair of fragments is produced due to the hydrogen atom migration from the hydroxyl group to the carbon atom via the 4-term transient state. Two alternative decay channels are possible here differing by both the reaction rate and the final charge localization:

The intensity of the corresponding peaks in the mass-spectrum may characterize the efficiency of the above reaction channels. According to our data, the intensity of the $m=44$ a.m.u. peak is higher than that of the $m=31$ a.m.u. peak, thus, in case of the C–C bond dissociation accompanied by the hydroxyl group H atom migration; the cation center is mainly displaced to the CO_2 fragment and the neutral CH_3NH_2 fragment is eliminated.

The ion with the $m=28$ a.m.u. mass is the second intensity-related peak in the parent molecule spectrum and may have the following gross formula: CH_2N or CO (or $CH_2N + CO$). In [33], it was suggested that this peak is due to the CH_2N^+ and/or CO^+ ions. However, the mass-spectra of the deprotonated glycine (with the $HNCD_2CO_2H$ and $H^{15}NCH_2CO_2H$ composition) show that this fragment contains a nitrogen atom, while the experiment for the deuterated $d5$ and $d3$-glycine [27] has unambiguously shown that this peak belongs to the CH_2N^+ (CD_2N^+) ion. The comparison of the stability of the positively charged ions CH_2N^+ and CO^+ (i.e., the binding energy per atom in eV calculated by us), also allows one to conclude that formation of the CH_2N^+ cation is more probable than that of the CO^+ cation.

The structure of the CH_2N^+ ion depends on the parent or intermediate ion bonds being broken. Four possible relevant isomers are shown in Figure 7. It is important that in cases when different bonds of the CH_4N^+ or CH_3N^+ cation are broken the fragments become planar after the geometry optimization. Calculations [27] have shown that the HCNH structure is the most stable of those presented in Figure 7. According to our calculations, when the geometry optimization performed with the B3LYP cc-pVTZ approach application, the trans- and cis-isomers (III and IV in Figure 7) transit to the most stable structure with the linear configuration (the point group C_s). Note that the C and N atoms in this case undergo the sp-hybridization.

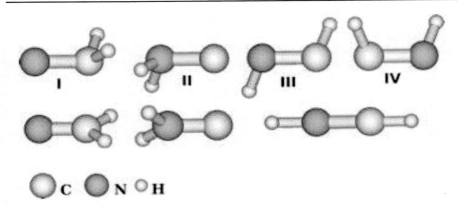

O C $\bullet$ N $\circ$ H

Figure 7. The CH_2N^+ glycine molecule cation isomers before (top) and after (bottom) the geometry optimization.

Experimentally the CH_3N^+ and CH_2N^+ cations are observed in the mass-spectrum (Figure 4). These positively charged ions could be produced at the simultaneous break of several simple bonds:

$$C_2H_5NO_2 + e \rightarrow \begin{cases} (CHO_2 + H)^- + CH_3N^+ + e; & (29) \\ (CHO_2 + H)^0 + CH_3N^+ + 2e; & (30) \\ (CHO_2 + H)^+ + CH_3N^+ + 3e & (31) \end{cases}$$

and

$$C_2H_5NO_2 + e \rightarrow \begin{cases} (CHO_2 + 2H)^- + CH_2N^+ + e; & (32) \\ (CHO_2 + 2H)^0 + CH_2N^+ + 2e; & (33) \\ (CHO_2 + 2H)^+ + CH_2N^+ + 3e. & (34) \end{cases}$$

Calculated energies required to produce the below fragments are presented in Tables 3 and 4. It is obvious that dissociation of the C–C bond with simultaneous detachment of one/two hydrogen atom(s) from the parent ion and production of the positive CH_2N^+ and CH_3N^+ ions require more energy than those in the case corresponding to pathway (25). However, as shown in Tables 3 and 4, no direct correlation between the required energy and the number of detached H atoms is observed. In case of process (30), formation of the CH_3N^+ ion occurs with minimal energy consumption. As shown in [34, 35], the H atom hopping from the amino group to the carbonyl group prior to dissociation of the C–C bond is one of the preferred dissociation channels after single photon ionization of the glycine molecule. So for the case of electron impact ionization this mechanism is the most energetically favorable when the CH_3N^+ fragment appeared.

Table 3. Calculated appearance energies (eV) for the CHO_2 + H and CH_3N cations/ anions

CH_3N (m=29 a.m.u.) charge	$(CHO_2 + H)$ (m=30 a.m.u.) charge	Glycine molecule geometry not changed*	Glycine molecule geometry changed**
1	-1	14.89	11.55
1	0	16.51	10.52
1	1	26.76	23.61

*,** – see explanatory notes in Table 2.

Table 4. Calculated appearance energies (eV) for the CHO_2 + 2H and CH_2N cations/ anions

CH_2N (m=28 a.m.u.) charge	$CHO_2 + 2H$ (m=30 a.m.u.) charge	Glycine molecule geometry not changed*	Glycine molecule geometry changed**
1	-1	19.45	12.89
1	0	20.2	14.63
1	1	29.32	23.02

*,** – see explanatory notes in Table 2.

Our analysis of the charge distribution for the $[CHO_2 + H]$ group (Table 5) shows that the minimal energies in Table 4 correspond to the production of the CH_2O_2 compound.

Table 5. Charge distribution in the $[CHO_2 + H]$ fragment group

Total charge	After optimization**		Before optimization* (Mulliken charge)	
	CHO_2	H	CHO_2	H
0	CH_2O_2 compound formed		0	0
1	1	0	1	0
-1	CH_2O_2 compound formed		-1	0

*,** – see explanatory notes in Table 2.

Thus, the break of the C–C bond accompanied by the H atom migration from the amino group to the carbonyl group oxygen is the most probable channel of the CH_3N^+ fragment formation. On the other hand, the positively charged CH_3N^+ and CH_2N^+ ions could result from the secondary dissociation due to deprotonation of the CH_4N^+ ions, while the CH_2N^+ ion could also appear due to deprotonation of the CH_3N^+ ion. For example, the above processes could be as follows:

$$CH_4N^+ \rightarrow \left\{ \begin{array}{l} H^0 + CH_3N^+ \\ (H + H)^0 + CH_2N^+ \end{array} \right. \quad \begin{array}{l} (35) \\ (36) \end{array}$$

$$CH_3N^+ \rightarrow \left\{ \begin{array}{l} H^0 + CH_2N^+ \\ (H + H)^0 + CHN^+. \end{array} \right. \quad \begin{array}{l} (37) \\ (38) \end{array}$$

The glycine molecule mass spectrum (Figure 4) reveals a diffuse peak at about $m^* \sim 26.1$ a.m.u. corresponding to the transition $30 \rightarrow 28$ with the detachment of the neutral fragment with the $m=2$ a.m.u mass, i.e., the secondary fragmentation of the CH_4N^+ ion. Thus the dehydration proceeds according to pathway (36) producing the molecular hydrogen we have observed experimentally.

In the course of deprotonation of the CH_4N^+ and CH_3N^+ fragments, the C–H or the N–H bonds could be broken. We have checked these two cases. The obtained energy values required to deprotonate CH_4N^+ and CH_3N^+ are presented in Table 6.

Table 6. Calculated energies (in eV) of the CH_4N^+ and CH_3N^+ ion deprotonation

Process	–C–H bond broken		–N–H bond broken	
	Glycine molecule geometry not changed*	Glycine molecule geometry changed**	Glycine molecule geometry not changed*	Glycine molecule geometry changed**
$CH_4N^+ \rightarrow H^0 + CH_3N^+$	4.84	5.36	5.92	5.58
$CH_3N^+ \rightarrow H^0 + CH_2N^+$	3.71	3.27	6.72	6.04

*,** – see explanatory notes in Table 2.

It should be mentioned that production of the CH_3N^+ ions under the C–H bond break in CH_4N^+ is more probable due to the latter ion stability that is higher than that of the CH_3N cations with the N–H bond being broken during the deprotonation of CH_4N^+. Additional comparison of the appearance energy for the CH_3N^+ cations leads to the conclusion that the reaction with the C–H bond break during the deprotonation of CH_4N^+ is more relevant. However, the production of the molecular hydrogen at the CH_4N^+ ion dehydration occurs, evidently, with the C–H and N–H bonds break.

We have calculated the energy spent for the C–N bond dissociation in the initial molecule. The possible dissociation channels are presented below:

$$C_2H_5NO_2 + e \rightarrow \begin{cases} C_2H_3O_2^- + NH_2^+ + e\,; & (39) \\ C_2H_3O_2^0 + NH_2^+ + 2e; & (40) \\ C_2H_3O_2^+ + NH_2^- + e; & (41) \\ C_2H_3O_2^+ + NH_2^0 + 2e\,. & (42) \end{cases}$$

Table 7. Calculated energies (in eV) of the glycine molecule dissociation into the $C_2H_3O_2$ and NH_2 fragments

$C_2H_3O_2$ (m=59 a.m.u.) charge	NH_2 (m=16 a.m.u.) charge	Glycine molecule geometry not changed*	Glycine molecule geometry changed**
-1	1	15.73	14.33
0	1	16.95	16.09
1	-1	14.84	12.88
1	0	14.9	12.98

*,** – see explanatory notes in Table 2.

In the mass spectra, the intensity of the ions produced at the above bond dissociation is ~1.59% for the m=16 a.m.u. and 0% for m=59 a.m.u. fragments. Thus, the amino group detachment from the parent molecule is less probable, despite the relatively low values of calculated energies required to break the C–N bond (see (41) and (42) and Table 7).

As mentioned above, the weak peak at m=28.5 a.m.u. (Figure 5) is of particular interest. Obviously, it could be assigned to the doubly charged $C_2H_3ON^{2+}$ ion. The single-charged $C_2H_3ON^+$ ion with m=57 a.m.u. in the glycine mass-spectrum [8] has the intensity of 0.4%, however, in the mass spectra of other α-amino acids, the fragment with this mass is very typical together with the fragments having masses m=30, 44 and 75 a.m.u. [29].

Moreover, the tandem mass spectrometry spectra of the deprotonated glycine marked by the D and ^{15}N isotopes reveal the most pronounced peaks at m=57–59 a.m.u. [33]. The replacement of two hydrogen atoms at the positions H8, H10 (Figure 6) by deuterium indicates that the formation of a water molecule takes place at the hydrogen atom detachment from the amine group. In [21], the 7-stage fragmentation trajectory of one of the glycine conformers was calculated. It has been shown that a water molecule is formed and released within the time of 3 ps due to the transition of the hydrogen atom from the amine group to the oxygen atom of the hydroxyl group. According to the authors of this paper, the optimization of the fragments favors the formation of the neutral water molecule and the positive glycine fragment over the ionic water and the neutral glycine fragment. In accordance with [29], the loss of a water molecule by the $CH_2NH_2COOH^+$ (m/z=75) fragment is accompanied by the metastable ion production with m*=43.3 a.m.u. In our case, the diffuse peak with this mass is not observed, while the small intensity of the peak at m=57 a.m.u. indicates the lack of fragmentation channel leading to the single-charged CH_2NHCO^+ ion formation. Thus, formation of the doubly charged CH_2NHCO^{2+} ion occurs, probably, simultaneously (during 10^{-5}–10^{-7} s) with water molecule elimination, which, in turn, becomes possible after the two-electron loss by the parent molecule from the first two highest occupied molecular orbitals (i.e., non-bonding n-orbitals of the nitrogen atom and the oxygen atom of the hydroxyl group). Since we seem to be the first to observe the above doubly charged ion in the amine acid mass spectra, we have calculated the total energy for some possible relevant ions. Thus, the CHO_2^{2+}, $C_2H_3O_2^{2+}$, $C_2H_3ON^{2+}$, $C_2H_2ON^{2+}$, $C_2H_3ON^{2+}$, $C_2H_2ON^{2+}$ ions were investigated. It should be mentioned that only the $C_2H_3O_2^{2+}$, $C_2H_3ON^{2+}$ and $C_2H_2ON^{2+}$ ions are stable, although their stability is not very high (Table 8). Hence, analyzing the data of Table 8, one may conclude that in our experimental conditions the most stable ion is produced.

Table 8. Binding energy per atom (in eV) for the relevant doubly charged ions

Ion	$C_2H_3O_2^{2+}$ (m/z=29.5)	$C_2H_3ON^{2+}$ (m/z=28.5)	$C_2H_2ON^{2+}$ (m/z=28)
Binding energy per atom	0.50	1.63	1.015

Calculation of the energy required to produce the doubly charged $C_2H_3ON^{2+}$ ion from the neutral molecule with multiplicity 1 shows that the H atom detachment from the C atom proceeds with a higher probability than that from the N atom, and in this case the minimal energy corresponds to the neutral [OH + H] fragment group (Table 9).

Table 9. Calculated energies (in eV) of the neutral glycine molecule dissociation into the $C_2H_3ON^{2+}$ and [OH + H] fragments

$C_2H_3ON^{2+}$	[OH + H] charge	Before optimization*	After optimization**
C-H bond broken	-1	48.4	36.8
	0	38.87	24.55
	1	35.33	27.0
N-H bond broken	-1	47.96	41.13
	0	38.44	28.89
	1	34.9	31.34

*,** – see explanatory notes in Table 2.

The results obtained indicate that in the $[OH + H]^0$ and $[OH + H]^-$ case a water molecule should be produced. Unfortunately, weak intensity of the $C_2H_3ON^{2+}$ ion peak did not allow us to measure the dissociative ionization function for this ion and to determine its appearance energy experimentally.

We have studied the possible mechanisms of the glycine molecule fragmentation by slow monoenergetic electrons. The experimental observations of the ionized fragment formation were supported by relevant theoretical calculations, predicting possible fragmentation paths. The analysis of the theoretically calculated channels of the main ion production from the glycine molecule (CH_4N^+) and the experimental dissociative ionization function for this ion, measured earlier, show that the stepwise structure of this curve may be due not only to the ionization of the parent molecule molecular orbitals, but also due to the charge change of the complementary particle produced.

The above calculations allowed us to suggest the most energetically beneficial dissociation channels for the glycine molecule with the charge of all produced particles to be taken into account. This extends the possibilities of the commonly used qualitative approach in the electron-impact mass spectrometry that takes into account the positive ions only, while the charge of the complementary fragmentation products is not detected and is taken to be zero.

Production of the doubly charged CH_2NHCO^{2+} fragment was observed for the first time. The assumption about the mechanism of production of this fragment by a simultaneous elimination of two electrons and a water molecule is confirmed by the calculation results according to which the least energy consumption corresponds to the C-H bond break being accompanied with the neutral [OH + H] fragments yield.

4.2. Methionine

The initial area of the methionine molecule mass-spectrum measured by us at the 70 eV electron energy (Figure 8) is generally close to that published in the NIST database [8]. The methionine molecule image and the atom numbers used are presented in Figure 9.

The main peculiarity of the methionine molecule as compared to other amino acid molecules that impact the electron interaction process is the presence of a sulfur atom in the side chain being bound with the two carbon atoms (see Figure 9).

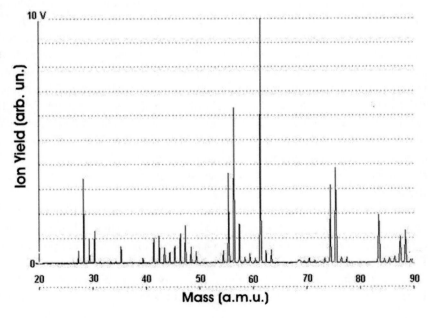

Figure 8. The initial area of the methionine molecule mass spectrum measured at the 70 eV electron energy.

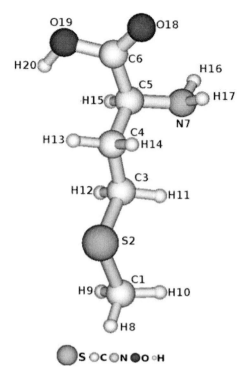

Figure 9. General view of the methionine molecule.

Since the methionine molecule, beside the sulfur atom, comprises two isolated functional groups involving heteroatoms with lone pair electrons, while the carbonyl group comprises the π-electrons, its ionization could proceed on due to both electron loss from the non-bounding heteroatom n-orbitals and the elimination of the double-bond π-electron. However, from the thermodynamic viewpoint, in case of molecular ion dissociation, the charge should be located at the fragment with less ionization potential, i.e., in our case at the sulfur atom, since this atom possesses stronger electron donor properties as compared to the amine-, hydroxyl- and carbonyl- groups [36].

According to one of the methods of analyzing the regulations of organic molecules fragmentation based on the notions of charge localization in molecular ions the fragmentation most probably proceeds via the simple bonds nearest to the charge localization places, i.e., at the energies slightly exceeding the methionine molecule ionization potential the most probable is the C–S bond dissociation. At higher energies, when the electron energy is sufficient to ionize deeper molecular orbitals, the nitrogen and oxygen lone pair orbitals first at all, it will result in a dissociation of the neighboring bonds, producing, in general, more fragmentation channels.

In order to make quantitative estimation of the most probable methionine molecule dissociation channels we have calculated the ground-state molecule orbitals (MO) using the B3LYP/cc-pVTZ method to determine the atomic orbital contribution to MO. Table 10 presents the results of the MO calculation involving the valence atomic shell electrons only, since binding energies of core electrons are too large to influence the ion appearance energy. The ionization potential of the methionine molecule, according to the Koopman's theorem [37], is 6.21 eV and is determined by a lone pair electron of the sulfur atom what coincides with the result presented.

Note that the electron binding energies calculated by us differ from those presented in [38]. These differences are due to the different approaches applied for the evaluation of the electron binding energy. In [38], electron binding energies are determined within the outer-valence Green function (OVGF) method [39], which takes into account both the MO reorganization energy and electronic correlation through the expansion series associated with each MO energy, i.e., with each primary ionization event. The method has been recognized as providing very satisfactory results and proved that the ionized band was not related to the shake-up ionized state [40]. However, the above method is expensive either in the hard disk volume and/or the CPU time and usually is adopted in case when electron binding energies experimentally measured and calculated are compared. Thus, to avoid huge hard disk volume and the CPU time consuming, the ionization energies were calculated from the B3LYP/cc-pVTZ orbital energies, that are usually obtained with the errors much larger than 2 eV. Thus, we prefer to calculate the first ionization potential as the difference between the energy of both the molecule and its ion, while the results in Table 10 are shown only for orientation aiming to foresee the charge localization and determine, which orbital could be assigned to the specific fragmentation channel.

The total (binding) energy calculated at the equilubrum point is -800.27 a.u. and the total (binding) energy of cation is -799.976 a.u., so the ionization energy calculated as the difference in energies between the D methionine cation and neutral molecule is 0.30 a.u. or 8.09 eV. These values coincide excellently with the data of Dehareng and Dive [40] who calculated the vertical ionization energies for three methoinine conformers and one of the conformers had a first ionization energy of 8.09 eV.

Table 10. Description of the energy, bond type and molecular orbitals per atomic orbitals with the largest contributions for the methionine molecule calculated by the B3LYP/cc-pVTZ method

Energy, eV	Assignment	Description of the orbital per atomic orbital
-14.96	σ_p	-0.18 (2pz,C6)+ 0.16 (2py, N7)
-14.50	σ_p	0.27(2px,C1)
-13.31	π	0.13(2px, C4)+0.16(2py,C4)+N7(-0.19(2py,N7)-0.09(2px,N7)-0.08(2py,O18)-0.098(2pz,O18)
-12.62	π	-0.202 (2py,C3)-0.17 (2px,O18) +0.18 (2pz,O18)
-12.57	σ_p	0.22(2px,C6)+0.13(2py,C6)-0.12(2px,N7)-0.11(2py,N7)-0,20 (2px,O18)+0.21(2px,O19)
-12.08	σ_p	-0.24(2px,C1)+0.15 (2py,O18)+0.12(2pz,O18)
-11.87	π	-0.21(2px,C1)+0.23(2py,C1) -0.13 (2py,O18)
-11.70	π	0.13(2px,C1)+0.25(2py,C1)+0.13 (2py,O18)
-11.32	σ_p	-0.12 (2px,C3)-0.18(2pz,C3)+0.19(2pz,C4)-0.14(2px,O18)-0.16(2px,O19)
-10.87	σ_p	0.11(2px,O18)+0.38(2pz,O19)
-10.59	σ_p	0.22(2pz,C3)-0.18(2px,C4)-0.20(2py,C4)+0.10(2py,O18)
-10.17	π	-0.20(2py,C3)+0.26(2py,C4)
-9.70	σ_p	-0.22(2pz,C1)-0.12(2pz,C3)+0.13(2px,C3)-0.16(2pz,S2)+0.12(2px,O19)
-9.04	π	-0.33(2px,O18)+0.37 (2px,O19)
-8.52	σ_p	-0.15(2pz,C1)-0.09(2px,C1)-0.195(2px,S2)-0.12(2pz,S2)-0.20 (2px,C3)
-8.04	π	0.24(2py,O18)-0.37(2pz,O18)+0.11(2py,O19)
-6.94	π	(-0.309 (2pz))
-6.21	π	HOMO 0.29 (2py,S2)

The largest molecular orbital coefficients, the atom and the atomic orbital types of this atom are presented.

It is generally known that ionization energy represents the absolute minimum energy required to ionize the neutral particle concerned. The further fate of the molecular ion depends on the shape of its potential energy surface. If its potential energy is minimal and the level of its excitation is below the energy barrier for dissociation, the ion may exist for a very long time. Ions having the internal energy above the dissociation energy level will dissociate at some point leading to the appearance of fragment ions [41].

The intensity of the aliphatic amine molecular ion peaks in the mass spectra is very low due to the high probability of decay processes initiated by the cation-radical center localized on the amine group. However, methionine displays a rather different pattern. Firstly, because the sulfur atom lone pair is the HOMO, therefore, at low energies it is ionized more preferably than the nitrogen lone pair. Secondly, the sulfide group stabilizes the positive charge and reduces fragmentation [42]. In our mass-spectrum, the initial molecular ion peak has relative intensity about 20%, while the NIST data [8] give that from 13.7 to 28.0%, and this value exceeds greatly the share of the similar molecular ions in the other aliphatic amino acid mass spectra. Thus, ionization of a sulfur lone pair orbital evidently causes much less molecular fragmentation. The mass-spectrum itself is characterized by a low selectivity what indicates the lack of a dominant decay pathway for the molecular ion.

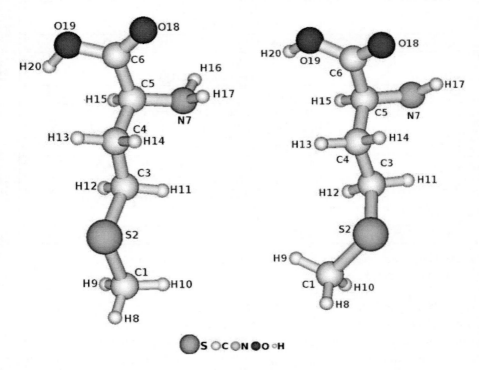

Figure 10. Neutral (left) and ionized (right) methionine molecule. The number of atoms in both figures remained the same.

It is known from the quantum-chemical calculations on determination of the geometry and interatomic distances of the optimized molecular structures for different organic molecules and their single-charged ions that the distances between the skeleton chain carbon atoms after ionization are resized (see, e.g., [43]). The electron loss by the molecule results in the fact that some skeleton bonds elongate, whereas the other bonds become a bit shorter. In this case the calculated value of the energy required for the C–C bond dissociation in the ionized molecules, depending on the fragmentation channels, is 0.84 to 3.45 eV [44].

To estimate the change in the methionine molecule geometry as the result of ionization, we have calculated both the bond lengths and the bond orders of the neutral and ionized methionine molecules at their equilibrium points (see Tables 11 and 12).

Table 11. Calculated methionine molecule bond lengths and orders

Bonds	Bond length, Å Neutral molecule	Bond order Neutral molecule	Bond length, Å Ionized molecule	Bond order Ionized molecule
C1-S2	1.886	0.938	1.886	0.903
C1-H8	1.087	0.935	1.085	0.910
C1-H9	1.087	0.924	1.087	0.902
C1-H10	1.087	0.924	1.087	0.897
S2-C3	1.899	1.024	1.877	0.981
C3-C4	1.525	0.886	1.531	0.809
C3-H11	1.091	0.897	1.094	0.873
C3-H12	1.086	0.917	1.088	0.892
C4-C5	1.553	0.906	1.576	0.865
C4-H13	1.093	0.947	1.091	0.934
C4-H14	1.093	0.936	1.091	0.915
C5-C6	1.539	0.854	1.566	0.851
C5-N7	1.456	1.008	1.429	0.976
C5-H15	1.096	0.925	1.090	0.913
C6-O18	1.222	1.969	1.216	1.927
C6-O19	1.386	0.951	1.359	0.999
N7-H16	1.012	0.876	1.009	0.844
N7-H17	1.014	0.869	1.013	0.825
O19-H20	0.978	0.805	0.978	0.788

Table 12. Dihedral angles between bonds and angles between planes

Bonds	Neutral molecule	Ionized molecule
	Angle, degrees	Angle, degrees
C1-S2-C3	98.62	102.83
S2-C3-C4	109.32	108.45
C3-C4-C5	111.87	109.46
C4-C5-N6	110.70	112.17
C4-C5-C7	109.43	105.57
C5-N7-O8	116.46	117.39
C5-N7-O9	124.26	120.66
S2-C1-H10	106.45	106.141
S2-C1-H11	110.26	109.29
S2-C1-H12	110.09	109.09
S2-C3-H13	108.65	117.87
S2-C1-H14	107.84	108.49
C3-C4-H15	109.80	111.72
C3-C4-H16	109.90	110.70
C4-C5-H17	108.20	109.43
C5-N6-H18	114.20	120.94
C5-N6-H19	113.13	118.27
C7-O8-H20	113.89	117.01
C1-S2-C3-C4	-175.94	124.101
S2-C3-C4-C5	178.88	172.21
C3-C4-C5-N6	-61.96	-56.43
C3-C4-C5-C7	173.02	-175.63
C4-C5-N7-O8	-73.30	-99.10
C4-C5-N7-O9	105.98	78.86
C3-S2-C1-H10	179.82	-176.71
C3-S2-C1-H11	-61.31	-57.59
C3-S2-C1-H12	61.00	64.05
C1-S2-C3-H13	-55.30	107.27
C1-S2-C1-H14	63.01	0.48
S2-C3-C4-H15	-58.74	-66.51
S2-C3-C4-H16	58.28	53.75
C3-C4-C5-H17	55.64	64.38
C4-C5-N6-H18	163.96	126.72
C4-C5-N6-H19	-68.41	-76.77
C5-C7-O8-H20	-0.86	-6.78

Having taken into consideration the results and implementing the Mulliken population analysis data [45], the weakest bonds in the methionine molecule were determined. The bond lengths calculated and bond orders of the neutral and ionized methionine molecule are listed in Table 11, while the changes in the geometry are shown in Figure 10 as well as in Table 12.

According to the results obtained for the neutral methionine molecule, the weakest bonds are C3–C4, C5–C6 and C4–C5. As a result of ionization, these bonds elongate, i.e., the probability of the molecular ion dissociation along these bonds increases. On the other hand, ionization of the molecule leads to the shortening of the carbon-heteroatom bonds, especially the C5–N7 bond, so deamination becomes improbable.

The highest peak in the methionine molecule mass-spectrum (Figure 8) corresponds to the $C_2H_5S^+$ ion ($m=61$ a.m.u.), which is complementary to the $C_3H_6NO_2^+$ ion ($m=88$ a.m.u.) due to the rupture of the weakest bond C3-C4 of the molecule. Hence, the results indicate clearly that substitutes influence the fragmentation process and allow us to predict that under the low-energy electron impact the rupture of the substitutes containing sulphur could be more probable than that of the core of amino acids. This prediction is confirmed by the results of calculations presented below.

Calculated appearance energies for the above fragments are listed in Table 13. The appearance energy E_{ap}, similarly to case of glycine, was calculated as:

$$E_{ap} = |E_{meth}| - |\Sigma(E_i)|.$$

here E_{meth} is the total energy of the neutral methionine molecule, while E_i is the total energy of all fragments produced. As mentioned above, this calculation does not take into account the activation energy of the molecular ion fragmentation.

This pair of fragments is formed at a simple break of the weakest C3–C4 bond of the initial molecule, and the charge is mainly localized at the fragment comprising the sulfur atom.

In this case the sulfur atom addiction to ionization and decay initiation are clearly seen. Inclusion of any possible cases of charge distribution at this bond dissociation results in the production of the C_2H_5S and $C_3H_6NO_2$ fragments according to the following pathways:

$$C_5H_{11}NO_2S + e \rightarrow \begin{cases} C_2H_5S^+ + C_3H_6NO_2^- + e & (43) \\ C_2H_5S^+ + C_3H_6NO_2^0 + 2e & (44) \\ C_2H_5S^- + C_3H_6NO_2^+ + e & (45) \\ C_2H_5S^0 + C_3H_6NO_2^+ + 2e & (46) \end{cases}$$

The most energetically favorable channels of the above cations formation correspond to pathways (43) and (45). Comparison of the intensities of the peaks leads to the prediction that formation of the $C_2H_5S^+$ cation is more probable than that of $C_3H_6NO_2^+$, although the opposite conclusion could be made from the result of the appearance energies calculated (Table 13). Thus, the binding energies per atom for these cations were calculated as well, and the results obtained prove that the above $C_2H_5S^+$ cation appears to be more stable than $C_3H_6NO_2^+$. It could be the main reason for that in the mass spectrum the peak at $m=61$ a.m.u. is more intense than that at $m=88$ a.m.u.

Table 13. Calculated appearance energies (eV) for the C_2H_5S and $C_3H_6NO_2$ fragments

C_2H_5S ($m=61$ a.m.u.) charge	$C_3H_6NO_2$ ($m=88$ a.m.u.) charge	Methionine molecule geometry not changed*	Methionine molecule geometry changed**
1	-1	13.71	7.17
1	0	14.53	10.71
-1	1	13.49	8.43
0	1	14.29	8.72

*,** – see explanatory notes in Table 2.

The complementary ions $C_2H_5S^+$ and $C_3H_6NO_2^+$ with low intensities were observed in the photoionization spectra at the 8.43 eV photon energy. At 11.62 eV their intensities are almost the same, while starting with 16.67 eV the peak at $m=61$ a.m.u. corresponding to the $C_2H_5S^+$ ion dominates [42].

The analysis of both the electron impact (EI) and photoionization (PI) mass spectra show that the main channel of the methionine molecule fragmentation above 16 eV is related to the rupture of the β-bond with respect to the sulfur atom. However, the appearance energy for this experimentally obtained in this work ion (12.4±0.1 eV) (see also [46]) allows us to conclude that this channel is not related only to the removal of a lone-pair electron from the sulfur atom. To make this ionization channel dominant, the ionization of at least of the third-highest occupied MO is required with further charge stabilization on the sulfur atom.

The next prominent peak in the mass-spectrum of the methionine molecule is due to the formation of the parent molecule fragment $C_3H_6N^+$ with the $m=56$ a.m.u. mass. This fragment may conceivably arise due to elimination of the CH_3SH and COOH fragments. In the PI and EI spectra, the peaks with the $m=104$ a.m.u. and $m=101$ a.m.u. masses corresponding to (M^+-COOH) and (M^+-CH_3SH) are present (here M^+ is a molecular ion produced at the initial molecule ionization). The intensities of these peaks in the PI spectra below 11.62 eV exceed the intensity of the peak of the $m=56$ a.m.u. fragment. At higher photon energies (>16 eV), the intensity inversion of these peaks is observed. It should be noted that at photon energies below 16 eV the efficiency of the PI channels, related to the rupture of the C3–S2 and C5–C6 bonds, is higher than that of the channel related to dissociation of the weakest C3–C4 bond leading to the $C_2H_5S^+$ fragment formation. Thus, the removal of the n_s-electron (or the HOMO-ionization) results in the appearance of fragmentation channels related to the dissociation of the C3–S2 and C5–C6 bonds. Obviously, the positive charge in this case is localized not on the sulfur but on the nitrogen atom.

The CH_3S+H and COOH fragments could be removed at the same time or it may be the two-step process. Some relevant results are presented in Tables 14 and 15. The lowest energy is reached when the $CH_3S + H$ fragments are joined to the CH_4S molecule. Theoretical investigations prove that the removal of the H13 atom requires the smallest amount of energy, thus the CH_4S molecule is produced due to the H13 atom migration to the sulfur atom via the 4-term transient state.

The appearance energy for the $C_3H_6N^+$ ion, measured in our experiment is 11.2±0.1 eV and it is higher than the calculated one. So, the process of simultaneous formation of the $(CH_4S + COOH)$ and $C_3H_6N^+$ fragments from the neutral methionine molecule under EI is not realistic.

Table 14. Calculated appearance energies (eV) for the C_3H_6N and $CH_4S +$ COOH fragments of the neutral methionine molecule

C_3H_6N ($m=56$ a.m.u.) charge	$CH_4S + COOH$ charge	Methionine molecule geometry not changed*	Methionine molecule geometry changed**
1	-1	9.16	1.24
1	0	9.63	4.38

*,** – see explanatory notes in Table 2.

Table 15. Calculated energies (in eV) required for the C_3H_6N and CH_4S fragment formation from the methionine molecule with the loss of the COOH fragment

C_3H_6N (m=56 a.m.u.) charge	CH_4S charge	(M^+-COOH) geometry not changed*	(M^+-COOH) geometry changed**
1	-1	8.06	2.93
1	0	10.04	1.73
1	1	18.86	11.16

*,** – see explanatory notes in Table 2.

Thus, the calculations of the energies required for the $C_3H_6N^+$ and CH_4S fragments formation from the methionine molecule after the loss of the CO_2H fragment, were carried out (Table 15).

In fact, Table 15 presents the excess energy of the $C_4H_{10}NS^+$ ion required for its subsequent fragmentation with the production of the $C_3H_6N^+$ ion. The experimental difference in the appearance energies E_{ap} for the m=104 a.m.u. and m=56 a.m.u. fragments measured in this work (as well as in [29]) is 1.5±0.2 eV, thus, the general pathway for the cascade process is as follows:

$$C_5H_{11}NSO_2 + e \rightarrow C_4H_{10}NS^+ + COOH^0 + 2e$$
$$\searrow C_3H_6N^+ + CH_4S^0. \qquad (47)$$

It should be noted that the geometrical and electronic structures of the C_3H_6N fragment could be different because of the removal of different H atoms. Our calculations show that the removal of the H13 atom requires the smallest amount of energy. From the results of the comparison of the appearance energies as well as from the cation energy itself, we predict that the positively charged ion with the m=56 a.m.u. mass has the form presented in Figure 11.

In this case, the C3–C4–C5 atoms are located on one plane at the angle of 120.57°, i.e., the hybridization of the carbon atoms is changed: $sp^3 \rightarrow sp^2$, and the pseudoconjugation system is formed involving a single unsaturated moiety and an atom with a lone pair of electrons in the p-orbital. Electron delocalization occurs over three atoms.

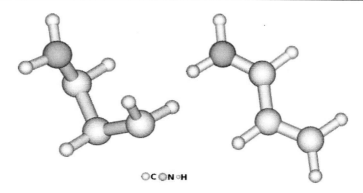

$\bigcirc$C $\bigcirc$N $\circ$H

Figure 11. View of the m=56 a.m.u. cation when the methionine molecule geometry is not changed (left) and when the equilibrium geometry of the cation is reached (right).

The next prominent peak in the mass-spectrum of the methionine molecule is due to the formation of the fragment with the mass of m=30 a.m.u. Such a peak is characteristic for alkyl amines and usually dominates in the mass-spectra of the relevant compounds.

On the basis of the results of our investigations, it was concluded that the assignment of this peak is related to the formation of the CH_4N^+ fragment [46]. It should be mentioned that formation of the CH_4N^+ fragment from the alkyl amines with side chains is complicated because not only the electron-impact induces the bond cleavage, but also the rearrangement of one hydrogen atom upon fragmentation is required.

The CH_4N^+ fragment could be formed according to the following pathways:

$$C_5H_{11}NO_2S + e \rightarrow \begin{cases} (CH_3N+H)^- + (COOH+C_3H_6S)^- + e & (48) \\ (CH_3N+H)^+ + (COO+C_3H_7S)^- + e & (49) \\ (CH_3N+H)^- + (COO+C_3H_7S)^0 + 2e & (50) \\ (CH_3N+H)^- + (COOH+C_3H_6S)^0 + 2e & (51) \end{cases}$$

The hydrogen atom attachment to CH_3N^+ is followed by the energy release of 6.12 or 7.85 eV respectively, when H originates from the C_3H_7S or COOH fragment, respectively. Thus, the hydrogen atom from the hydroxyl group takes part in the CH_4N^+ fragment formation. In this case, the lowest energy is required to divide the methionine molecule into the $(COO + C_3H_7S)^-$ anion and the CH_4N^+ cation.

The fragment peak CH_4N^+ ($m=30$ a.m.u.) in the methionine molecule mass spectrum is accompanied by the satellite peaks with the masses of $m=28$ a.m.u. and $m=29$ a.m.u.

The fragment with the mass of $m=29$ a.m.u. may be assigned to the COH^+ or CH_3N^+ ion. According to the results of theoretical investigation, it is possible to state that in the case of methionine the COH fragment could not be formed because there is no possibility to form the $C_4H_{10}NS + O$ compound, i.e., the probability of the simultaneous C–O and C–C bonds rupture is very low. Hence, the fragment with $m=29$ a.m.u. could be the CH_3N^+ cation. The lowest appearance energy for this fragment is required when the methionine molecule is divided into the ion pair according to the following pathway (when the initial geometry of the methionine molecule is not changed):

$$C_5H_{11}NO_2S + e \rightarrow CH_3N^+ + (COOH + C_3H_7S)^- + e. \qquad (52)$$

Despite the fact that production of the CH_3N^+ fragment takes place at the minimal number of structural changes as compared to the production of the ions with $m=30$ a.m.u. and $m=28$ a.m.u., the intensity of the peak with $m=29$ a.m.u. is lower as compared to that with $m=30$ a.m.u. or $m=28$ a.m.u. Such a pattern of the peak intensity distribution is an argument in favor of the hypothesis that the driving force of the molecular ion decay is not the charge localization at the heteroatom with the further break of the closest to it bonds, but the stability of the dissociation products. It should be noted that the calculated appearance energy for the CH_3N^+ fragment is at least 3.48 eV higher than that for the $(CH_3N + H)^+$ fragment. On the basis of these results we predict that the electron-impact fragmentation of methionine producing the $(CH_3N + H)^+$ fragment is more probable than that for the CH_3N^+ fragment.

The ion with the $m=28$ a.m.u. mass in the case of methionine contrary to glycine may have the following gross formulae: CH_2N, CO and C_2H_4. Comparison of the values of the binding energy per atom indicates that the CO^+ ion is less stable than the CH_2N^+ and $C_2H_4^+$ ones. Hence, observation of the CH_2N^+ and $C_2H_4^+$ fragments due to the electron impact is more probable than that for CO^+. Evidently that the CO^+ fragment could be produced according to the following pathways:

$$C_5H_{11}NO_2S + e \rightarrow CO^+ + (HO + C_4H_{10}NS)^- + e; \qquad (53)$$

$$C_5H_{11}NO_2S + e \rightarrow CO^+ + (HO + C_4H_{10}NS)^0 + 2e. \qquad (54)$$

Calculated appearance energies are presented in Table 16. It is clearly seen that the appearance energy of the CO^+ fragment according to the pathways given above is higher than the measured energy value (11.9$\pm$0.1 eV). The results described make it possible to predict that the positively charged fragment with the mass $m=28$ a.m.u. could not be the CO^+ ion.

Table 16. Calculated appearance energies (in eV) for the CO and (HO + C$_4$H$_{10}$NS) fragments of the methionine molecule

CO fragment charge	(HO + C$_4$H$_{10}$NS) fragment charge	Geometry not changed**	Geometry changed**
1	-1	17.66	15.53
1	0	18.50	14.92

*,** – see explanatory notes in Table 2.

Hence, two ways of formation of the CH$_2$N fragment were investigated because this fragment could be produced when two C–C and C–H or N–H bonds of the methionine are ruptured. It implies that the CH$_2$N fragment could have structures just like those presented in Figure 7 for the glycine molecule. The analysis of the appearance energies for the CH$_2$N$^+$ fragment produced from the neutral and ionized molecule shows that the calculated appearance energy of 11.83 eV according to the pathway

$$C_5H_{11}NO_2S^+ \rightarrow CH_2N^+ + (CHO_2 + H + C_3H_7S) \qquad (55)$$

coincides with the measured value (11.4$\pm$0.1 eV). However, in the near-threshold energy region production of the CH$_2$N$^+$ ion may be caused by some other mechanisms.

The positively charged CH$_3$N$^+$ and CH$_2$N$^+$ ions could result from the secondary dissociation of the CH$_4$N$^+$ ion, while the CH$_2$N$^+$ ion could also appear due to deprotonation of the CH$_3$N$^+$ ion. The above secondary dissociation is more possible in case when the energy transferred to the initial molecule increases.

As in the case of glycine, the methionine molecule mass spectrum reveals a diffuse peak at the mass of about m^*~26.1 a.m.u. (see Figure 12, the semi-logarithmic scale should be noted here) that corresponds to the 30→28 transition with the detachment of a neutral fragment with $m=2$ a.m.u., i.e., the secondary fragmentation of the CH$_4$N$^+$ ion occurs.

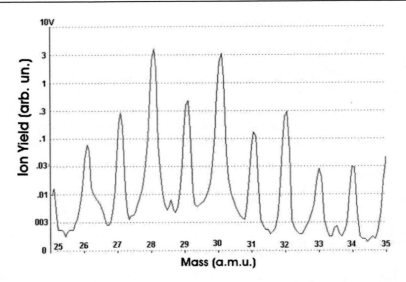

Figure 12. Low-mass area of the methionine molecule mass spectrum measured at the 70 eV electron energy.

Taking into account the measured appearance energy values for the CH_2N^+ and CH_4N^+ fragments (11.4 ± 0.1 and 11.0 ± 0.1 eV, respectively) and those calculated for these ions produced from the initial molecule, one may assume that in the near-threshold energy region the main mechanism of the CH_2N^+ ion production is a cascade dissociation via the CH_4N^+ ion formation:

$$C_5H_{11}NO_2S^+ \rightarrow CH_4N^+ + C_4H_7O_2S^0 \rightarrow CH_2N^+ + H_2 + C_4H_7O_2S^0$$

(56)

Due to this dehydration, when the stable hydrogen molecule is formed as the dissociation product, the fragment with the mass of $m=29$ a.m.u. is difficult to be produced as well.

We assign the peak at the $m=45$ a.m.u. mass to the $COOH^+$ fragment because to produce the above fragment the rupture of only the C5–C6 bond is required, while formation of other isobaric fragments, such as CHS^+ and $C_2H_7N^+$, require a break of several bonds and, in some cases, the rearrangement of the hydrogen atoms. On the other hand, it should be noted, that the loss of COOH, NH_2 and $COO+NH_3$ together with formation of $COOH^+$ are the major channels of the methionine molecule dissociative ionization [47]. Different processes of the $COOH^+$ fragment formation have been analyzed by us:

$$C_5H_{11}NO_2S + e \rightarrow \begin{cases} CHO_2^- + C_4H_{10}NS^+ + e & (57) \\ CHO_2^0 + C_4H_{10}NS^+ + 2e; & (58) \\ CHO_2^+ + C_4H_{10}NS^- + e & (59) \\ CHO_2^+ + C_4H_{10}NS^0 + 2e & (60) \end{cases}$$

It is possible to notice that the lowest energy required to divide the methionine molecule aiming to form the CHO_2^+ cation corresponds to pathway (58). The experimentally measured appearance threshold for this fragment is 13.5±0.1 eV. The comparison of this value with the data from Table 8 shows that the production of the CHO_2^+ fragment may be proceeded via channels (59) and (60).

It should be noted that, according to pathways (57–60), the fragment with the $m=104$ a.m.u. mass is formed. By comparing the calculated and measured (9.7±0.1 eV) appearance energies for this positively charged ion, the conclusion can be made that dissociation with the $C_4H_{10}NS^+$ ion production from the parent ion proceeds according to pathways (57) and (58).

Table 17. Calculated appearance energies (in eV) for the CHO_2 and $C_4H_{10}NS$ fragments

CHO_2 ($m=45$ a.m.u.) charge	$C_4H_{10}NS$ ($m=104$ a.m.u.) charge	Methionine molecule geometry not changed*	Methionine molecule geometry changed**
-1	1	10.01	7.35
0	1	10.77	8.7
1	-1	14.98	12.34
1	0	14.24	11.76

*,** – see explanatory notes in Table 2.

Since the COOH and $C_4H_{10}NS$ fragments are complementary, the intensity of the corresponding peaks in the mass-spectrum may characterize the efficiency of the above reaction channels. According to our data, the intensity of the peak at $m=104$ a.m.u. is higher than that of the peak at $m=45$ a.m.u., thus, in case of the C5–C6 bond dissociation the cation center is mainly displaced to the $C_4H_{10}NS$ fragment.

The mechanism of the $C_4H_{10}NS^+$ fragment formation required the C5–C6 bond the molecular ion to be broken. This could be visualized as the β-decay towards the nitrogen atom producing the immonic structure typical in the dissociative ionization of amines, where the nitrogen atom is capable of the effective stabilization of the positive charge:

$$HOOC-CHR-\overset{..}{N}H_2 \xrightarrow{-e} HOOC-CHR-\overset{+}{N}H_2 \longrightarrow \overset{.}{C}OOH + CHR=\overset{+}{N}H_2$$

$$(61)$$

Here R is an amino acid side chain. In the case of methionine R is C_3H_7S. The one-electron shift ($\frown$) from the ionized nitrogen atom and α-carbon atom results in formation of a double bond accompanied by energy release.

The peak at $m=46$ a.m.u. in the mass-spectrum of the methionine molecule is assigned to the $CH_2O_2^+$ ion. The above ionized fragment may be produced according to the following pathways:

$$C_5H_{11}NO_2S + e \rightarrow \begin{cases} (H+CHO_2)^+ + C_4H_9NS^0 + 2e \rightarrow CH_2O_2^+ + C_4H_9NS^0 + 2e & (62) \\ (H+CHO_2)^+ + C_4H_9NS^- + e \rightarrow CH_2O_2^+ + C_4H_9NS^- + e & (63) \end{cases}$$

The calculated appearance energy of the ion when the neutral $C_4H_9NS^0$ is formed is equal to 13.22 eV, while in the case of $C_4H_9NS^-$ formation this energy is equal to 12.59 eV. These two values are close to the measured appearance energy (13.1 ± 0.1 eV). Thus, we predict that both reactions are possible. It should be emphasized that several different possibilities to form the ion with $m=46$ a.m.u. were also investigated. However, only in one case the calculated and measured appearance energy values fit very well. This is the case when methionine looses the COOH group and the H13 atom joins CHO_2 to form $CH_2O_2^+$.

The peaks at $m=74$ a.m.u. and $m=75$ a.m.u. are present in the mass-spectrum with almost equal intensities. At first sight, these two fragments are complementary and are formed due to the C4–C5 bond rupture. However, the satellite peaks at $m=76$ a.m.u. and $m=77$ a.m.u. with the intensities of 7.47% and 4.47%, respectively, considering the contribution of ^{13}C to $m=76$ a.m.u., allow us to state that both fragments with the $m=74$ and $m=75$ a.m.u. masses include the sulfur atom, thus confirming the statement of Junk and Svec [29]. The fragment with $m=75$ a.m.u. (i.e., $C_3H_7S^+$) is produced due to the C4–C5 bond dissociation, whereas the fragment at $m=74$ a.m.u. (i.e., $C_3H_6S^+$) is formed as a result of the hydrogen atom migration in the transient complex with the subsequent dissociation of the skeleton C4–C5 bond. In this case the neutral fragment is detached and its structure corresponds to the glycine molecule.

Calculation of the appearance energies for the $C_2H_4NO_2^+$ (m=74 a.m.u.) and $C_3H_7S^+$ (m=75 a.m.u.) ions at the C4–C5 bond dissociation shows that the energy minimum corresponds to the formation of an ion pair (Table 18). Comparison of the calculated appearance energies for these fragments allows us to conclude that the process $C_4H_{11}NSO_2+e \rightarrow C_2H_4NO_2^- + C_3H_7S^+ +e$ requires the minimal energy consumption.

Table 18. Calculated appearance energies (eV) for the $C_2H_4NO_2$
and C_3H_7S fragments

$C_2H_4NO_2$ (m=74 a.m.u.) charge	C_3H_7S (m=75 a.m.u.) charge	Methionine molecule geometry not changed*	Methionine molecule geometry changed**
-1	1	11.83	8.07
0	1	13.12	8.96
1	-1	12.98	7.85
1	0	13.46	9.79

*,** – see explanatory notes in Table 2.

The peak at m=83 a.m.u. is present in the mass spectrum with a moderate intensity. On the basis of a simple analysis (mass calculation of all possible fragments formed due to any bond rupture) we may predict that the fragment with m=83 a.m.u. is the product of several short-run processes. In [42], it was assumed that this fragment is produced due to a cascade fragmentation of the methionine molecule via the formation of the ion with the m=131 a.m.u. mass (due to the loss of H_2O), and the further loss of the CH_3SH neutral fragment. The $C_4H_5ON^+$ fragment may have either the cyclic structure of the amine-derived furan or the linear one (Figure 13). It is necessary to note, that the $C_4H_5ON^+$ cation is divided into the C_3H_5N and CO fragments at the equilibrium point. Meanwhile the mechanism of production of this fragment and its structure is not experimentally established. The minimal number of structural transformations corresponds to elimination of H_2O with hydrogen transfer to the sulfur atom and with the C3–S2 bond rupture.

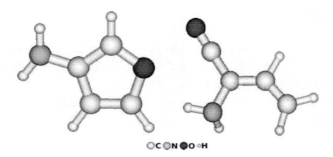

Figure 13. View of the $C_4H_5ON^+$ fragment with the amine-derived furan (left) and linear (right) structure.

Note that the measured appearance energy of the $m=101$ a.m.u. fragment $(C_4H_7NO_2^+)$ is 7.5 ± 0.1 eV and this value is less than the calculated HOMO binding energy in [38]. The experimental ionization energy of the parent molecule is about 8.6 eV [8, 38, 48]. Hence, formation of the positive $C_4H_7NO_2^+$ ion proceeds from the vibrationally excited initial neutral molecule with the detachment of the negative CH_3SH^- fragment. It should be mentioned that the geometrical structure of the $C_4H_7NO_2^+$ cation could be different due to the different $-C-H$ bond rupture, i.e., different migration of H atoms. All possible isomers of this cation were studied theoretically by us. The structure of the cation obtained shows that its formation is due to the H13 hydrogen atom migration to the sulfur atom and the rupture of the S2–C3 bond with no change in the initial structure of molecule. At higher energies, beginning from 11.0 ± 0.1 eV, the same processes lead to the appearance of the CH_4S^+ fragment. This means that at electron energies below the ionization threshold the positive charge is localized on the $C_4H_7NO_2$ fragment, whereas, at higher energies, this occurs on the sulfur-containing fragment.

The peak at $m=131$ a.m.u. in the methionine molecule mass-spectrum is assigned to $C_5H_9NOS^+$ and corresponds to elimination of the fragment(s) with $m=18$ a.m.u. This dissociation channel dominates at the photon energy of 8.43 eV. The above ionized and neutral fragments may be produced according to the following pathways:

$$C_5H_{11}NO_2S + e \rightarrow \begin{cases} C_5H_9NOS^- + (OH+H)^+ + e & (64) \\ C_5H_9NOS^0 + (OH+H)^+ + 2e & (65) \\ C_5H_9NOS^+ + (OH+H)^- + e & (66) \\ C_5H_9NOS^+ + (OH+H)^0 + 2e & (67) \end{cases}$$

Comparison of the experimental and calculated data shows that formation of the $C_5H_9NOS^+$ ion (m=131 a.m.u.) at the parent molecule dissociation is not accompanied by detachment of two fragments (HO + H) (see Table 19). The energy release required to produce the neutral water molecule lowers the calculated appearance energy for the $C_5H_9NOS^+$ ion by 6.39 eV. Therefore, the appearance of the peak at m=131 a.m.u. in the methionine mass spectrum is related to the neutral water molecule elimination.

Table 19. Calculated appearance energies (eV) for the C_5H_9NOS fragment produced from the neutral methionine molecule

C_5H_9NOS (m=131 a.m.u.) charge	(HO + H) fragment charge	Methionine molecule geometry not changed*	Methionine molecule geometry changed**
-1	1	18.96	13.52
0	1	21	13.87
1	-1	15.21	13.35
1	0	18.68	10.81

*,** – see explanatory notes in Table 2.

The large-mass area of the methionine molecule mass spectrum (Figure 14) reveals a diffuse peak at about m^*~115.1 a.m.u. that corresponds to the 149→131 transition i.e., the elimination of the neutral fragment with m=18 a.m.u. Thus, the dissociation channel of the parent methionine molecule related to the neutral water molecule detachment was experimentally confirmed by us.

The methionine molecule mass-spectrum also reveals a peak at m=35 a.m.u. and its identification as belonging to the SH_3^+ fragment is at first sight doubtful. Indeed, formation of this fragment requires not only the break of two skeleton α-bonds with respect to the sulfur atom but also displacement of three hydrogen atoms. However, the experimental results prove that the peak at m=35 a.m.u. as that of the SH_3^+ one because it is accompanied by a satellite peak with m=37 a.m.u., the intensity of which corresponds to the natural ^{34}S isotope contribution.

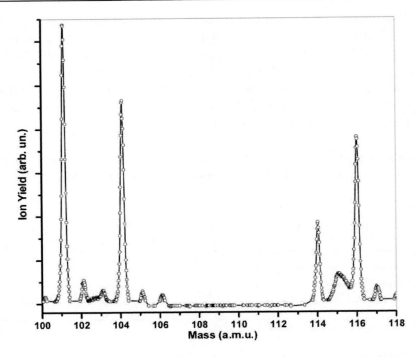

Figure 14. The large-mass area of the methionine molecule mass spectrum measured at the 70 eV electron energy.

Possibility to form the SH_3^+ cation when the C atom is removed from the CH_3S fragment is not confirmed, e.g., by the data on the methylthiole (CH_4S) and dimethyldisulfide (CH_3SSCH_3) mass spectrometry [5]. Both these compounds under electron impact produce the CH_3S^+ ion, though no SH_3^+ ion was observed in the relevant mass spectra. Our theoretical results exhibit the $6.27 - 6.44$ eV energy required to remove the C atom from the CSH_3^+ cation. On the other hand, the mass spectra of dialkyl sulfides (say, CH_3SCH or $C_2H_5SC_2H_5$) reveal the $CH_3SCH_2^+$ and SH_3^+ ions [8].

When the dialkyl sulfides have alkyl branching that blocks off the $CH_3SCH_2^+$ ion formation, the SH_3^+ ion is not produced as well. This indirectly confirms the cascade character of the fragmentation resulting in the SH_3^+ ion appearance. It should be mentioned that the possible mechanism of the SH_3^+ cation formation from $CH_3SCH_2^+$ via the cyclic transition state is described in [49]. Therefore, the analysis of the mass spectra of the low-molecular dialkyl sulfides allows us to conclude that the sulfonium ion in the methionine molecule mass-spectrum arises due to the cascade mechanism of the $CH_3SCH_2^+$ ion secondary dissociation.

The semi-logarithmic scale presentation of the initial area of mass-spectrum (see Figure 14) allowed the specific features (not discussed in the up-to-date papers) to be found, i.e., two weak peaks related to the doubly charged $C_2H_3ON^{2+}$ (m/z=28.5) and $C_4H_3O^{2+}$ or $C_4H_5N^{2+}$ (m/z=33.5) ions. We seem to be the first to observe the above doubly charged ions in the amine acid mass-spectra.

Obviously, the peak at m/z=28.5 is assigned to the doubly charged $C_2H_3ON^{2+}$ ion. This conclusion is made based on the basis of the results obtained in this chapter. In the methionine molecule mass-spectrum, the singly charged $C_2H_3ON^+$ ion with m=57 a.m.u. is present (Figure 8). This indicates that the parent molecule fragmentation according to the 'amine' type could lead to formation of both singly and doubly charged ions with the 57 a.m.u. mass. Most probably, formation of the $C_2H_3ON^{2+}$ ion under electron impact occurs as a result of dissociation of the skeleton C4–C5 bond of the doubly charged parent molecule ion accompanied by the water molecule elimination. Taking into account that the hydroxyl group and the hydrogen atom required for the water molecule formation are in the opposite parts of a parent molecule after the C4–C5 bond rupture, one may conclude that H_2O is eliminated simultaneously or slightly before the skeleton bond dissociates.

The results of optimization indicate that in the case of $[OH + H]^0$ and $[OH + H]^-$ a water molecule should be produced. Unfortunately, weak intensity of the $C_2H_3ON^{2+}$ ion peak did not allow us to measure the dissociative ionization function for this ion and to determine its appearance energy experimentally.

We suggest the following probable pathway of the doubly charged $C_2H_3ON^{2+}$ ion formation:

$$C_5H_{11}NO_2S + e \rightarrow C_5H_{11}NO_2S^{2+} + 3e \rightarrow C_2H_3ON^{2+} + (H_2O + C_3H_6S)^0 + 3e \quad (68)$$

As stated above, Figure 14 clearly illustrates an additional peak related to another doubly charged ion at m/z=33.5 a.m.u. No singly charged ion with the m=67 a.m.u. mass is present in the methionine molecule mass-spectrum. The gross formula of the doubly charged ion at m/z=33.5 may be $C_4H_3O^{2+}$ or $C_4H_5N^{2+}$. Obviously, formation of the doubly charged $C_4H_3O^{2+}$ ion occurs after elimination of the stable neutral fragments H_2O, NH_2, CH_4S from the doubly charged parent molecule ion (pathway 69). In the case of the $C_4H_5N^{2+}$ ion the parent doubly charged molecule eliminates H_2O, CH_4S and the oxygen atom (pathway 70). To check the possibility of the stepwise formation of this doubly charged ion we have analyzed the areas of the mass spectra where the possible intermediate ions may arise. The doubly charged $(M–H_2O)^{2+}$, $(M–$

$NH_2)^{2+}$ and $(M-CH_4S)^{2+}$ ions corresponding to the sequential detachment of neutral fragments from the parent ion are not observed in the methionine molecule mass-spectrum, what allows us to exclude the cascade process during formation of the ion with $m/z=33.5$. Different possibilities of the double-charged ion formation were theoretically investigated. The results obtained allow us to conclude that the possible channels of formation of the doubly charged ions at $m/z=33.5$ are as follows:

$$C_5H_{11}NO_2S + e \rightarrow C_5H_{11}NO_2S^{2+} + 3e \rightleftharpoons C_4H_3O^{2+} + NH_2^0 + H_2O^0 + CH_4S^0 + 3e \qquad (69)$$

$$C_4H_5N^{2+} + O^0 + H_2O^0 + CH_4S^0 + 3e \qquad (70)$$

We provided calculations concerning the stability of the doubly ionized fragments taking into account the structure of ions produced (Table 20).

Our calculations of the internal energy for cyclic and different linear structures of the $C_4H_3O^{2+}$ ion allow us to conclude that the linear structure is more stable than the cyclic one. But, according to our calculations, among the doubly charged ions with $m/z=33.5$ the most stable is the $C_4H_5N^{2+}$ one. The structure of this ion obtained after optimization, i.e., when the equilibrium geometry is achieved, is presented in Figure 15.

Table 20. Stability of the doubly ionized fragments with $m/z=33.5$

Fragment	Internal energy, a.u.	Energy of formation, eV	Energy of formation per atom, eV
$C_4H_5N^{2+}$	-209.164	30.237	3.022
$C_4H_3O^{2+}$ (O=C-C-CH-CH$_2$)	-228.328	18.894	2.362
$C_4H_3O^{2+}$ (O=C-CH-CH-CH)	-228.340	18.59	2.324
$C_4H_3O^{2+}$ (Cyclic form)	-228.240	16.17	2.022

○C ⊙C ●N ∘H

Figure 15. Structure of the $C_4H_5N^{2+}$ ion obtained after optimization.

Table 21. Appearance energies for the methionine molecule fragments

Fragment mass, a.m.u.	Ion assignment	Experimental appearance energy, eV	NIST data [8]	Calculated data	
				Appearance energy, eV	Other reaction products
28	CH_2N^+	11.4 ± 0.1	–	11.31^{**}	$(C_3H_7S + H + CHO_2)^0$
30	CH_4N^+	11.0 ± 0.1	–	9.08^{**}	$(COO + C_3H_7S)^0$
41	$C_3H_5^+$	13.3 ± 0.1	–	9.74^{**}	$(NH_2 + CH_3S + CHO_2)^0$
	$C_2H_3N^+$			14.41^{**}	$(CHO_2 + C_2H_5S + 2H)^-$
42	$C_3H_6^+$	12.9 ± 0.1	–	–	–
	$C_2H_4N^+$			9.37^{**}	$(C_2H_5S + H + CHO_2)^-$
				16.98^{**}	$(C_2H_5S + H + CHO_2)^0$
43	$C_3H_7^+$	13.2 ± 0.1		–	–
	$C_2H_5N^+$			13.58^*	$(C_2H_5S + CHO_2)^-$
				7.46^{**}	
44	$C_3H_8^+$	12.9 ± 0.1		–	–
	$C_2H_6N^+$			8.28^{**}	$(C_2H_5S + CO_2)^0$
	CS^+		–	16.76^{**}	$(CH_3 + 2H + C_3H_6NO_2)^0$
45	CHO_2^+	13.5 ± 0.1	–	11.76^{**}	$C_4H_{10}NS^0$
46	$CH_2O_2^+$	13.1 ± 0.1	–	13.22^{**}	$C_4H_9NS^{0,-1}$
47	CH_3S^+	13.0 ± 0.1	13.0 ± 0.20	11.82^{**}	$(C_4O_2NH_8)^0$
48	CH_4S^+	11.0 ± 0.1	–	10.57^{**}	$C_4H_7NO_2^0$
55	$C_3H_5N^+$	11.8 ± 0.1	–	11.86^{**}	$(CH_3S + 2H + CHO_2)^-$
56	$C_3H_6N^+$	11.2 ± 0.1	–	10.04^*	$(CH_3S + H + CO_2H)^0$
57	$C_3H_7N^+$	12.7 ± 0.1	–	12.51^{**}	$(CH_3S + CO_2H)^-$
61	$C_2H_5S^+$	12.4 ± 0.1	12.43 ± 0.10	10.71^{**}	$C_3H_6NO_2^0$
74	$C_3H_6S^+$	–		12.26^{**}	$C_2H_5NO_2^0$
	$C_2H_4NO_2^+$		–	9.79^{**}	$C_3H_7S^0$
75	$C_3H_7S^+$	–		8.07^{**}	$C_2H_4NO_2^-$
	$C_2H_5NO_2^+$		–	10.82^{**}	$C_3H_6S^-$
88	$C_3H_6NO_2^+$	–	–	8.72^{**}	$C_2H_5S^0$
101	$C_4H_7NO_2^+$	7.5 ± 0.1	–	9.26^{**}	$(CH_3S + H)^0$
104	$C_4H_{10}NS^+$	9.7 ± 0.1	9.68 ± 0.15	8.7^{**}	CHO_2^0
114	$C_5H_6OS^+$	9.3 ± 0.1	–	10.50^{**}	$(NH + OH + 3H)^-$
116	$C_5H_8OS^+$	8.5 ± 0.1		14.93^{**}	$(NH_2 + OH)^0$
	$C_5H_{10}NS^+$			14.37^{**}	$(OH + O)^-$
131	$C_5H_9NOS^+$	–	–	10.81^{**}	$(OH + H)^0$
149	$C_5H_{11}NO_2S^+$	8.6 ± 0.1	8.63 ± 0.10	8.09^{**}	–

*,** – see explanatory notes in Table 2.

Thus, after the loss of two electrons from the first two highest occupied molecular orbitals (i.e., non-bonding n-orbitals of the sulfur atom and the nitrogen atom) by the parent methionine molecule, formation of the doubly charged $C_2H_3ON^{2+}$ ($m/z=28.5$) and the $C_4H_5N^{2+}$ and/or $C_4H_3O^{2+}$ ($m/z=33.5$) ions becomes possible. However, among the last ones the presence of the $C_4H_5N^{2+}$ ion is more probable due to its stability.

As mentioned above, we have determined experimentally the appearance energies for the methionine molecule fragments and complemented them with the relevant calculations ([48]). Table 21 shows our experimental and theoretical appearance energy values for the methionine fragments as compared with the other data.

Please note that in some cases the appearance energies of some fragments were not calculated because there was no possibility to obtain these fragments from the methionine molecule in its equilibrium point and it was impossible to predict how the geometry of the methionine molecule could change when the above fragments are formed.

On the other hand, we have calculated the appearance energies of some fragments despite the fact that the experimental results for different reasons were not obtained. So, the intensity of the peak with $m=85$ a.m.u. is very weak, therefore it was not investigated experimentally although the results of theoretical investigations indicate that this fragment is $C_4H_5O_2^+$ and the energy of its appearance is equal to 11.17 eV.

However, despite all the modeling and calculations performed, the calculated appearance energy for the $m=116$ a.m.u. fragment is too high as compared to the value measured. We predict that this fragment, as well as those with $m=42, 43, 44$ a.m.u., are formed from the methionine not in its equilibrium state. Other possible for the formation states are difficult to be predicted or investigated.

4.3. Alanine

In the present study, the DL α-alanine in a form of a crystalline powder of a 99% minimal purity was used without any further purification. The views of the conformers of the α-alanine molecule are shown in Figure 16.

The conformers of the α-alanine may contain intramolecular hydrogen bonds, i.e., the alanine I has the asymmetric bifurcated H6$\cdots$O4$\cdots$H7 bonds and the O4$\cdots$H8 bond, while the alanine II has the H8$\cdots$N bond, and the alanine III has the NH$\cdots$O5 bond. According to our calculations, the total energies of the three most stable conformers of the α-alanine molecule differ insignificantly and the conformer II is the most stable one of them.

The results of our calculations agree well with those of other authors (see, e.g., [50]). However, calculated energies for the general amino acid isomers quoted by Blanco et al. [51] have different sequence order of total energy.

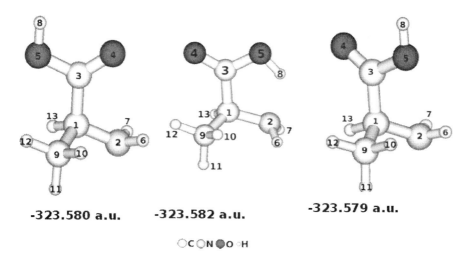

-323.580 a.u.   -323.582 a.u.

-323.579 a.u.

○C ○N ●O ○H

Figure 16. Views and calculated total energies of the neutral alanine molecule isomers: alanine I (left), alanine II (center) and alanine III (right).

According to his conclusion, the conformer I is the most stable one. Indeed, experimentally it is difficult to recognize the geometry of the most stable conformer directly, but, in general, the van der Waal's bonds may be formed between the atoms of these conformers.

The single explanation why the conformer I, where three (the largest number) hydrogen bonds may be formed, is less stable, is that the choice should be made between the several "equal" positions. It is known that the van der Waals' bond includes the following forces:
- the force between two permanent dipoles;
- the force between a permanent dipole and a corresponding induced dipole;
- the force between two instantaneously induced dipoles.

The permanent dipole formation depends mostly on the geometrical structure of the molecule, while induced dipoles are formed when electron density is shifted by a charged molecule, i.e., when the positively charged species are close to the species with an evenly distributed charge electrons go towards the side, where the positive species are present, and are away from the opposite side creating an artificial dipole molecule. Thus, in the alanine I isomer, where three bonds may be formed, the induced dipole is difficult to be formed because the oxygen atom electrons have three possible places to shift. It implies that these van der Waals' bonds are weaker than those in the alanine II isomer. On the other hand, this means that the alanine I isomer becomes more flexible because there is no one "permanent" van der Walls bond, but time by time one of the possible bond could be formed due to the molecule rotation and vibration.

For the hydrogen-bonded systems a structural rearrangement following ionization of such a molecule is quite typical [52]. Each conformer of alanine can have somewhat different fragmentation pathways associated with the intramolecular hydrogen bonding.

According to our theoretical investigations, the most stable conformer is the alanine II, the energy of which is 0.054 eV lower than that of the alanine I and the smallest energy barrier for the transition of the alanine III to the alanine I in the ground state due to rotation of the –COOH group is only 0.086 eV. The energy difference is approximately 0.02 eV when the alanine III transits to the alanine I, i.e., it is equal to the thermal energy kT at room temperature, while the above barrier is much smaller than the energy of the incident electron. Additionally, theoretical results exhibit that the equilibrium structure of the ionized alanine III molecule is like that of the alanine I molecule, i.e., the main structural difference between the alanine III and the alanine I disappears when these molecules are ionized. Thus, we intend to investigate theoretically fragmentation of the alanine I and alanine II conformers.

Tables 22 and 23 (see below) present the values of the calculated bond lengths and bond orders for the neutral and ionized alanine molecule conformers.

According to the results obtained for the neutral molecules, the weakest bonds are C1–C3 and O5–H8 ones. The C–C bond is the weakest in the glycine molecule too. Ionization of a parent molecule is most probably generated from the mixed σ_pN2-O3 orbital, which is the highest occupied molecular orbital. It includes the N2(0,41(2pz)); O3(0,13(2pz)) electron moiety and its energy (or the first ionization potential) calculated by the Koopman's theorem is 6.59 eV. However, the experimental and calculated values as the difference of the energies of the neutral and ionized molecules for the first ionization energy of alanine are above this level (even when the possible error up to 2 eV is taken into account) and lie within 8.75–9.85 eV [8, 27, 31]. This implies that ionization of the alanine molecule could proceed from the HOMO–1(σ_pC1-O4–O5, 7.997 eV) and HOMO–2 (π O4–O5, 9.048 eV) orbitals as well. Thus, it is obvious that ionization of the alanine molecule involves the $NH_2CHCOOH$ group directly.

Table 22a. The bond lengths of the alanine isomers I and II before and after ionization

Bonds	Alanine I		Alanine II	
	Bond length, Å Neutral	Bond length, Å ionized	Bond length, Å Neutral	Bond length, Å Ionized
C1–N2	1.433	1.415	1.483	1.415
C1–C3	1.578	1.588	1.535	1.604
C1–C9	1.530	1.556	1.535	1.523
C1–H13	1.096	1.087	1.093	1.101
N2–H6	1.020	1.017	1.011	1.017
N2–H7	1.020	1.017	1.012	1.016
C3–O4	1.389	1.212	1.228	1.210
C3–O5	1.386	1.349	1.360	1.348
O5–H8	0.982	0.984	1.002	0.984
C9–H10	1.090	1.089	1.091	1.089
C9–H11	1.090	1.090	1.093	1.091
C9–H12	1.090	1.089	1.089	1.089

As a result of ionization, the C1–C3 bond elongates for all structures investigated, i.e., the probability of the molecular ion dissociation along this bond increases. Electron density redistribution due to the molecule ionization leads to a noticeable reduction of the C1–N2 bond length and to the increase of its strength forcing the carboxyl group atoms to approach each other. This testifies to the low probability of the α-alanine molecule dissociation channels related to the rupture of the skeleton carbon atom bonds with heteroatoms. It is also interesting to note that due to ionization of the above three conformers the O5–H8 and C1–N2 bond lengths become the same.

The area of the alanine molecule mass-spectrum measured in our experiment at the 70 eV electron energy (see Figure 17) is generally close to that given in [8]. The main peculiarity of our mass-spectrum is the larger intensity of the peak at $m=18$ a.m.u. Furthermore, presentation of this spectrum using semi-logarithmic scale (inset in Figure 17) allowed the specific features not discussed in the up-to-date papers to be revealed, i.e., the weak peak related to the doubly charged $m/z=43.5$ ion and splitting of the $m/z=18$ peak are observed clearly.

**Table 22b. The bond lengths of the alanine isomer III
before and after ionization**

Bonds	Alanine III	
	Bond length, Å Neutral	Bond length, Å Ionized
C1–N2	1.455	1.415
C1–C3	1.528	1.604
C1–C9	1.542	1.522
C1–H13	1.092	1.101
N2–H6	1.011	1.016
N2–H7	1.012	1.017
C3–O4	1.230	1.210
C3–O5	1.379	1.348
O5–H8	0.981	0.984
C9–H10	1.088	1.090
C9–H11	1.093	1.091
C9–H12	1.090	1.088

**Table 23a. The bond orders of the alanine isomers
I and II before and after ionization**

Bonds	Alanine I		Alanine II	
	Bond order, neutral	Bond order, ionized	Bond order, neutral	Bond order, ionized
C1–N2	0.937	0.989	0.850	0.915
C1–C3	0.815	0.730	0.827	0.704
C1–C9	0.983	0.970	0.976	1.011
C1–H13	0.880	0.912	0.937	0.861
N2–H6	0.809	0.819	0.876	0.816
N2–H7	0.807	0.807	0.876	0.808
C3–O4	1.102	1.971	1.949	1.979
C3–O5	0.998	1.082	1.075	1.092
O5–H8	0.767	0.764	0.743	0.763
C9–H10	0.920	0.923	0.942	0.920
C9–H11	0.905	0.906	0.940	0.915
C9–H12	0.916	0.911	0.938	0.914

Table 23b. The bond orders of the alanine isomer III before and after ionization

Bonds	Alanine III	
	Bond order, Neutral	Bond order, Ionized
C1–N2	0.999	0.995
C1–C3	0.843	0.704
C1–C9	0.942	1.012
C1–H13	0.929	0.860
N2–H6	0.879	0.808
N2–H7	0.866	0.816
C3–O4	1.977	1.980
C3–O5	1.007	1.089
O5–H8	0.803	0.763
C9–H10	0.949	0.919
C9–H11	0.944	0.916
C9–H12	0.942	0.914

The peaks with $m=44, 42, 28, 18$ a.m.u. are the most noticeable in the α-alanine mass-spectrum. The absence of a clear parent molecular ion $C_3H_7NO_2^+$ peak (its intensity is about 0.2% of that for the maximal peak) indicates that probability of non-dissociative ionization for this molecule is negligible. The dominant peak in the experimental mass-spectrum corresponds to the ion with the $m=44$ a.m.u. mass, i.e., to the $NH_2CH_3CH^+$ ion formed via a single rupture of the C1–C3 bond (Figure 16). *Ab initio* calculations of the fragmentation channels for the α-alanine cation find this channel to be energetically most favorable. These results coincide with those presented in [53]. The rupture of the C1–C3 bond results in the production of the C_2H_6N and CHO_2 fragments:

$$C_3H_7NO_2 + e \rightarrow \begin{cases} C_2H_6N^- + CHO_2^- + e; & (71) \\ C_2H_6N^+ + CHO_2^+ + 3e; & (72) \\ C_2H_6N^+ + CHO_2^0 + 2e; & (73) \\ C_2H_6N^- + CHO_2^+ + e; & (74) \\ C_2H_6N^0 + CHO_2^+ + 2e; & (75) \end{cases}$$

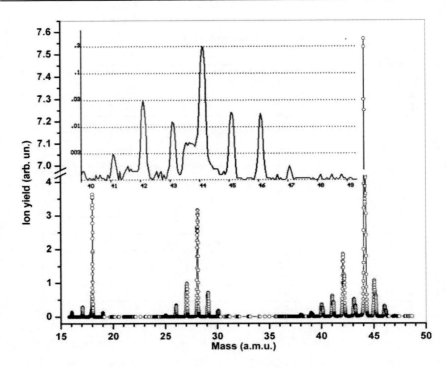

Figure 17. The initial area of the DL α-alanine molecule mass spectrum.

Calculated appearance energies for the above fragments are listed in Tables 24, 25.

Table 24. Calculated appearance energies (in eV) for the C_2H_6N and CHO_2 fragments formed from the alanine I molecule

C_2H_6N (m=44 a.m.u.) charge	CHO_2 (m=45 a.m.u.) charge	Alanine molecule geometry not changed*	Alanine molecule geometry changed**
1	-1	10.07	7.58
1	1	22.69	17.61
1	0	11.40	9.12
-1	1	16.60	13.16
0	1	15.29	12.08

*,** – see explanatory notes in Table 2.

Table 25. Calculated appearance energies (in eV) for the C_2H_6N and CHO_2 fragments formed from the alanine II molecule

C_2H_6N (m=44 a.m.u.) charge	CHO_2 (m=45 a.m.u.) charge	Alanine molecule geometry not changed*	Alanine molecule geometry changed**
1	-1	10.92	7.69
1	1	22.17	17.65
1	0	11.64	9.04
-1	1	15.78	13.20
0	1	14.60	12.12

*,** – see explanatory notes in Table 2.

The most energetically favorable channels of the $C_2H_6N^+$ cation formation correspond to pathways (71) and (74). Experimental results indicate that the appearance energy for the $C_2H_6N^+$ fragment ion under the electron-impact ionization of the gas phase L-alanine determined from the measured ion efficiency curves is 9.10±0.05 eV [8], while that of the DL-alanine measured by us is 9.30±0.1 eV. In the photoionization experiment [27], the appearance energy for this fragment ion is 9.05±0.10 eV.

These results allow us to conclude which of the channels (73) is more probable for the optical isomers of the alanine molecule and this agrees with the results of other authors. It should be noted that calculated value of the appearance energy for the $C_2H_6N^+$ cation from the L-alanine molecule listed in [8] is 9.51 eV and is larger than that determined experimentally. Calculated values of the appearance energies for this fragment formed from the alanine I (9.12 eV) and the alanine II (9.04 eV) coincide perfectly with the thermochemical value 9.12 eV calculated based on the data on the heat of formation and with the data presented in [27] as well as with those obtained experimentally. Hence, the results exhibit clearly that the appearance energies of the same fragment from different conformers are different.

We have checked the possibility of CO_2^+ formation at dissociative ionization of the alanine molecule. Calculated results indicate that production of this ion is energetically non-favorable because its appearance energy is approximately twice larger than that for the isobaric $C_2H_6N^+$ fragment. It should be mentioned that the appearance energy for the CO_2^+ ion presented in [54] is 3 eV smaller than the value obtained by us as the smallest appearance energy of the CO_2^+ fragment for the DL-alanine molecule. Summarizing previously mentioned, it is possible to conclude that the peak at m=44 a.m.u. in the experimental mass spectrum could be attributed to formation of the $C_2H_6N^+$ fragment.

It should be noted that in case of the C1–C3 bond dissociation in the initial molecule the complementary fragment with the 45 a.m.u. mass is produced. Calculated appearance energy for this ion is 12.08 eV for the alanine I molecule and 12.12 eV for the alanine II molecule. In this case, the presence of the hydrogen bond O4···H8 in the alanine I and alanine III molecules favors this fragment stability during the C1–C3 bond dissociation.

In the mass range of 40–47 a.m.u. (see Figure 18), a very small peak at $m=42$ a.m.u. was observed experimentally. This peak may be attributed to the presence of the CH_3CHN^+ (or $C_2H_4N^+$) ion, although Jochims et al. [27] and Ipolyi et al. [54] identified this fragment as $NH_2CH_2=C^{\cdot+}$ and $CH_3C\equiv NH^+$, respectively. Our decision is based on the analysis of the bond order of the neutral isomers that indicates that the C1–C3, N2–H7 and N2–H6 bonds are weaker than other C–H bonds (see Table 23). On the other hand, we suggest another structure for this fragment not mentioned among the possible structures calculated for this stoichiometry. Hence, the above fragments may be produced according to the following pathways:

$$C_3H_7NO_2+ e \rightarrow \begin{cases} C_2H_4N^+ + (H+H+CHO_2)^- + e; & (76) \\ C_2H_4N^+ + (H+H+CHO_2)^+ + 3e; & (77) \\ C_2H_4N^+ + (H+H+CHO_2)^0 + 2e. & (78) \end{cases}$$

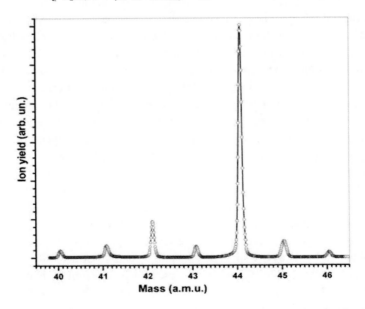

Figure 18. The area of the DL α-alanine mass spectrum in the 40–47 a.m.u. mass region.

Table 26. Calculated appearance energies (in eV) for the C_2H_4N and $(H+H+CHO_2)$ fragments formed from the alanine I molecule

C_2H_4N (m=42 a.m.u.) charge	$H + H + CHO_2$ charge	Alanine molecule geometry not changed*	Alanine molecule geometry changed**
1	-1	19.68	10.08
1	0	20.87	11.74
1	1	31.26	20.18

*,** – see explanatory notes in Table 2.

Table 27. Calculated appearance energies (in eV) for the C_2H_4N and $(H+H+CHO_2)$ fragments formed from the alanine II molecule

C_2H_4N (m=42 a.m.u.) charge	$H + H + CHO_2$ charge	Alanine molecule geometry not changed*	Alanine molecule geometry changed**
1	-1	19.70	10.18
1	0	22.39	12.09
1	1	30.89	19.93

*,** – see explanatory notes in Table 2.

The results of the appearance energy studies for this fragment indicate the pathway (76) to be more favorable for the I- and II-alanine (Tables 26, 27). Theoretical values of 10.08 and 10.18 eV obtained for the I- and II-alanine, respectively, coincide with the experimental one of $(9.87\pm0.1$ eV) [54] proving the assumption that the alanine isomers could be ruptured producing the $C_2H_4N^+$ ionic fragment via the ion pair formation according to pathway (76). The results of the geometry optimization of the $H+H+CHO_2$ charged compound indicate that the neutral H_2 molecule could be formed, although in the present study the above results are of no importance.

The appearance energies for the $C_2H_4N^+$ ions with different structural isomers calculated in the present study are closer to the experimental value than the *ab initio* result (10.87 eV) presented in [55], where it was stated that the CH_3CNH^+ ion is formed via the following reaction process: $C_3H_7NO_2^+ \rightarrow CH_3CNH^+ + HCO^- + H_2O$. Note, that in both pathways the $C_2H_4N^+$ ion appears in a case of an ion pair formation. Thus, the mechanism of the $C_2H_4N^+$ ion production includes the detachment of a carboxyl group from the initial molecule accompanied by the molecular hydrogen formation according to pathway (76) rather than the disintegration process of the COOH group and the water molecule elimination as suggested in [54].

As emphasized above, the present calculations result in the values that coincide well with the experimental ones. Note that optimization results indicate changeability of the initial CH_3CHN^+ ion geometrical structure. The fragment CH_3CHN^+ transforms to CH_3NCH^+ at its equilibrium point. We started optimization from the CH_3CNH^+ structure and finally obtained the CH_3-N-CH^+ structure. Geometrical structures of the $C_2H_4N^+$ ion before and after optimization are shown in Figure 19.

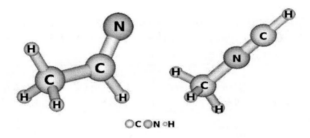

$$\bigcirc C \quad \bigcirc N \quad \circ H$$

Figure 19. Views of the CH_3CHN^+ fragment when alanine is ruptured (left) and at the equilibrium point (right).

The mechanism of the structural change during formation of the above ion could take place via the intermediate cyclic structure of the dehydrated ethylene imine according the pathway given below

$$CH_3CNH^+ \longrightarrow \underset{CH}{\overset{H_2C-NH^+}{\diagdown\diagup}} \longrightarrow CH_3NCH^+$$

This intermediate structure is possible to be obtained when analyzing the optimization process. The bond order analysis indicates that in the $C_2H_4N^+$ positive ion structure the double bonds are formed between both the N and C atoms, while the bond order between the C–C atoms is 0.846. Thus, this bond is the weakest one in the intermediate cyclic structure and the above bond rupture is possible. In the obtained structure, the C1 atom undergoes, obviously, the sp-hybridization.

Based on the results described above, we state that the pathway

$$C_3H_7NO_2 + e \rightarrow C_2H_4N^+ + (H+H+CHO_2)^- + e \rightarrow CH_3NCH^+ + (H_2+CHO_2)^- + e$$

is more probable than any other one mentioned in [54].

The ion with the $m=28$ a.m.u. mass is the second intensity-related peak in the parent molecule spectrum and is accompanied by the satellite peaks with the $m=27$ a.m.u. and $m=29$ a.m.u. masses. The area of the DL-alanine molecule mass spectrum in the 26.5–29.5 a.m.u. region presented in the semi-logarithmic scale is shown in Figure 20.

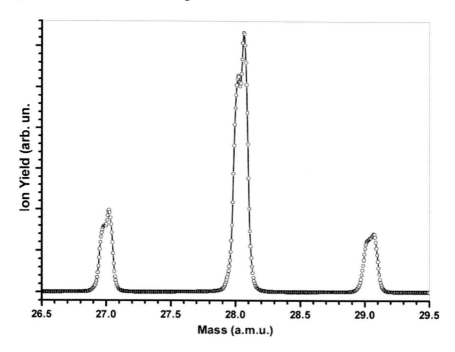

Figure 20. The area of the DL α-alanine mass spectrum in the 26.5–29.5 a.m.u. mass region.

It is obvious that all three peaks in this figure have double-headed shape, so at least two ions may contribute to each peak. As to the $m=27$ a.m.u. peak, Jochims et al. [27] assigned it to the $C_2H_3^+$ ion rather than to the HCN^+ one and confirmed this conclusion by the α-alanine-$d3$ electron impact mass spectrum. Our spectra show the presence of the two of these isobaric ions with nearly close intensities but some preference is given to the $C_2H_3^+$ ion. A double-headed peak with the $m=29$ a.m.u. mass is due to the two components and consists of the HCO^+ and NH_2CH^+ ions with some preference being given to the HCO^+ ion. It should be noted that deuteration of the α-alanine molecule does not help to choose between these two possible assignments [27] and our results show that both ions are formed in the collision event.

The $m=28$ a.m.u. ion is an intense fragment in the α-alanine mass spectrum and may have the following gross formulae: CH_2N, C_2H_4 and CO. Jochims et al. [27], Ipolyi et al. [54] and Bari et al. [55] assigned it exceptionally to the $HCNH^+$ ion, but Lago et al. [56] identified this peak as consisting of the $HCNH^+$ and CO^+ ions. In our spectrum, only two distinct peaks arise in the vicinity of the 28 a.m.u. mass.

However, the calculated binding energy per atom for $C_2H_4^+$ is 0.31 eV larger than that for CH_2N^+ and is 1.23 eV larger than that for the CO^+ ion. The comparison of stability of the $C_2H_4^+$, CH_2N^+ and CO^+ ions allows us to conclude that $C_2H_4^+$ is more stable than CO^+ and CH_2N^+. In case of methionine [46], we have shown that formation of the CO^+ ion is energetically less probable than that of the $C_2H_4^+$ and CH_2N^+ ions. The same was observed for the case of alanine as well.

As for the calculated appearance energies of these $C_2H_4^+$ and CH_2N^+ fragments (see Tables 28–31), note that they are a bit different. Thus, in case of the $C_2H_4^+$ ion, the appearance energy is in both cases under study smaller by more than 4 eV if the alanine molecule geometry was not changed. It implies that if the fragment energy is minimal and the level of its excitation is below the energy barrier for dissociation, the appearance of the $C_2H_4^+$ ion is more probable. If the ions have the internal energy above the dissociation energy and reach their equilibrium geometry, the results become a bit contradictory. For the ion pair formation, the appearance of the CH_2N^+ ion seems to be more probable. When the positively charged ion and the neutral ftagment are formed, the appearance energy values become very close, so both the $C_2H_4^+$ and CH_2N^+ ions might arise. Thus, we may conclude that two isobaric ions peaks with the $m=28$ a.m.u. mass in the experimental spectra belong to the $C_2H_4^+$ and CH_2N^+ ions and the channel of the $C_2H_4^+$ ion formation is more efficient at the 70 eV collision energy than that of the CH_2N^+ ion.

Table 28. Calculated appearance energies (in eV) for the C_2H_4 and (NH_2+COOH) fragments formed from the alanine I molecule

C_2H_4 ($m=28$ a.m.u.) fragment charge	NH_2 + COOH fragment charge	Alanine molecule geometry not changed*	Alanine molecule geometry changed**
1	-1	15.97	13.44
1	0	17.89	11.80

*,** – see explanatory notes in Table 2.

Table 29. Calculated appearance energies (in eV) for the C₂H₄N and (NH₂+COOH) fragments formed from the alanine II molecule

C_2H_4 (m=28 a.m.u.) charge	$NH_2 + COOH$ charge	Alanine molecule geometry not changed*	Alanine molecule geometry changed**
1	-1	15.38	12.08
1	0	17.31	12.21
1	1	26.30	

*,** – see explanatory notes in Table 2.

Table 30. Calculated appearance energies (in eV) for the CH₂N and (COOH + H +CH₃) fragments formed from the alanine I molecule

$C-NH_2$ (m=28 a.m.u.) charge	$COOH + H + CH_3$ charge	Alanine molecule geometry not changed*	Alanine molecule geometry changed**
1	-1	21.08	9.98
1	0	21.69	12.41
1	1	31.92	19.51

*,** – see explanatory notes in Table 2.

Table 31. Calculated appearance energies (in eV) for the CH₂N and (COOH + H +CH₃) fragments formed from the alanine II molecule

$C-NH_2$ (m=28 a.m.u.) charge	$COOH + H + CH_3$ charge	Alanine molecule geometry not changed*	Alanine molecule geometry changed**
1	-1	19.92	8.94
1	0	21.09	12.45
1	1	31.29	19.55

*,** – see explanatory notes in Table 2.

One may emphasize that in our previous papers [48, 57] the glycine and the methionine molecule mass spectra revealed a diffuse peaks at about m*~26.1 a.m.u. corresponding to the transition 30→28 being accompanied by the detachment of a neutral fragment with m=2 a.m.u., i.e., the secondary fragmentation of the CH_4N^+ ion occurred. However, in the case of the α-alanine, this dissociation channel was not observed by us. Thus, dehydration process according to the pathway $CH_4N^+ \rightarrow (H + H)^0 + CH_2N^+$ is not realized in the electron-impact-induced α-alanine molecule fragmentation.

We have calculated the CH_2N^+ ion production from different conformers of the α- alanine with different bonds being ruptured. When the equilibrium geometry structure of the alanine molecule fragments is taken into account, the smallest appearance energies were obtained when CH_2N^+ was formed according to the following general pathways:

$$C_3H_7NO_2 + e \rightarrow \begin{cases} CH_2N^+ + (COOH + H + CH_3)^- + e; & (79) \\ CH_2N^+ + (COOH + H + CH_3)^0 + 2e; & (80) \\ CH_2N^+ + (COOH + H + CH_3)^+ + 3e. & (81) \end{cases}$$

Calculated energies required to produce the fragments discussed above are listed in Tables 30 and 31.

It was mentioned in [54] that the ion production efficiency curve for the L-alanine molecule fragment with the $m=28$ a.m.u. mass exhibits two distinct thresholds at 10.85 eV and 12.8 eV. In [27], the CH_2N^+ ion-yield curve exhibits an initial onset at 9.00 ±1 eV and a sharp rise in the signal at 12.35 eV, and this, according to the point of view of the authors, was considered as a second onset energy attributed to the loss of H_2 from primarily formed $NH_2CH_2^+$. The analysis of the results allows us to predict that the thresholds at the $NH_2CH_2^+$ fragment appearance from the alanine I and the alanine II could be close to those mentioned above. It implies that the stepwise structure of this ion yield curve may be due not only to the different pathways of the parent molecule dissociation but also to the change of the charge of the complementary particles produced. Thus, according to our calculations, the process corresponding to a pathway (79) with ion pair production is energetically more favorable.

According to the qualitative mass-spectrometry theory, where the direction of fragmentation of the molecule under study is defined by the stability of the fragments produced, formation of the CH_2N^+ ion seems to be most probable according to the following pathways:

$$C_3H_7NO_2^+ \rightarrow CH_2N^+ + (CH_3 + CO_2 + 2H) \rightarrow CH_2N^+ + (CH_3 + CO_2 + H_2) \quad (82)$$

and

$$C_3H_7NO_2^+ \rightarrow CH_2N^+ + (CH_3 + CO + (OH+H)) \quad (83)$$
$$\searrow H_2O$$

Thus, the fragments that may be produced in this case are the stable molecules and the radical. In our calculations, both these reactions were studied, but, unfortunately, the last process appeared impossible to be calculated from the very beginning (i.e., when the parts of the alanine molecule were used) because there was some intermediate reaction resulting in the formation of the CO and OH fragments.

Calculated appearance energies for reaction (82) are listed in Tables 32, 33 (see also Tables 34, 35). Calculated appearance energy is similar to the experimental one in case of production of two positively charged fragments, however, this process seems to be impossible in the near-threshold appearance energy area for the $m=28$ ion.

Table 32. Calculated appearance energies (in eV) for the CH_2N and CH_3 + CO_2 + 2H fragments formed from the alanine I molecule

CH_2N ($m=28$ a.m.u.) charge	$CH_3 + CO_2 + 2H$ charge	Alanine molecule geometry not changed*	Alanine molecule geometry changed**
1	-1	15.21	0.36
1	0	15.50	3.87
1	1	28.64	11.83

*,** – see explanatory notes in Table 2.

Table 33. Calculated appearance energies (in eV) for the CH_2N and CH_3 + CO_2 + 2H fragments formed from the alanine II molecule

CH_2N ($m=28$ a.m.u.) charge	$CH_3 + CO_2 + 2H$ charge	Alanine molecule geometry not changed*	Alanine molecule geometry changed**
1	-1	18.40	0.95
1	0	19.79	3.59
1	1	30.75	10.97

*,** – see explanatory notes in Table 2.

Our calculations of the appearance energy for the CH_2N^+ fragment according to the pathway (82) show that this process is not realized during the alanine molecule electron-impact dissociation, i.e., the system does not reach its equilibrium state. Despite the minimal consumption of the energy required to produce the final products according to pathway (82), the experimental appearance energies for the CH_2N^+ fragment are most adequately described by pathways (79) and (80).

The structure of the CH_2N^+ ion depends on the parent or intermediate ion bonds being broken and is shown in Figure7. Calculation shows that the most stable structure of the CH_2N fragment is H13–C1–N2–H6.

Table 34. Calculated appearance energies (in eV) for the CH_2N and ($COOH + H + CH_3$) fragments formed from the alanine I molecule

HC–NH (m=28 a.m.u.) charge	$COOH + H + CH_3$ charge	Alanine molecule geometry not changed*	Alanine molecule geometry changed**
1	-1	20.22	9.48
1	0	20.89	12.12
1	1	31.19	19.50

*,** – see explanatory notes in Table 2.

Table 35. Calculated appearance energies (in eV) for the CH_2N and ($COOH + H + CH_3$) fragments formed from the alanine II molecule

HC–NH (m=28 a.m.u.) charge	$COOH + H + CH_3$ charge	Alanine molecule geometry not changed*	Alanine molecule geometry changed**
1	-1	21.32	8.94
1	0	22.66	12.45
1	1	32.52	19.56

*,** – see explanatory notes in Table 2.

For the ion with m=18 a.m.u. there are two possible compositions, i.e., H_2O^+ and NH_4^+. The yield curve for the m/z=18 ion measured in [54] has a threshold at 12.55±0.1 eV. Since this value is within the limits of an experimental error of the ionization energy determination for water 12.62±0.002 eV, the authors concluded that the fragment with m/z=18 results from ionization of the water molecule, while formation of the NH_4^+ ion was not observed in [54], most probably, due to the fact that the cross section for this reaction is very low.

On the other hand, in [27] the m/z=18 ion was assigned to NH_4^+ with HC–CH–COOH as a neutral product. Referring to the analysis of the mass-spectra for the α-alanine-$d3$ molecule, the authors stated that the NH_4^+ ion contains two amino hydrogen atoms and two hydrogen atoms originally attached to the carbon skeleton. Formation of the NH_4^+ ion involves rearrangement processes, but the hydrogen atom attached to the carboxyl group is not favored as a participating migrant one. According to the relative intensities of the $m/z=17$ and $m/z=18$ peaks in the mass spectrum, the authors determined the maximum contribution of H_2O^+ to the $m=18$ a.m.u. peak at the 20 eV photon impact to be about 5% [27].

As seen from Figure 17, the yield of the ion with the $m=18$ a.m.u. mass in our experiment is higher than that in the other studies and is comparable to the $m=28$ a.m.u. ion yield. Semi-logarithmic presentation of our mass-spectrum within the 15–20 a.m.u. mass range (see Figure 21) allowed splitting of the $m=18$ a.m.u. peak to be found that confirms experimentally the presence of the H_2O^+ and NH_4^+ ions produced during the alanine molecule dissociative ionization.

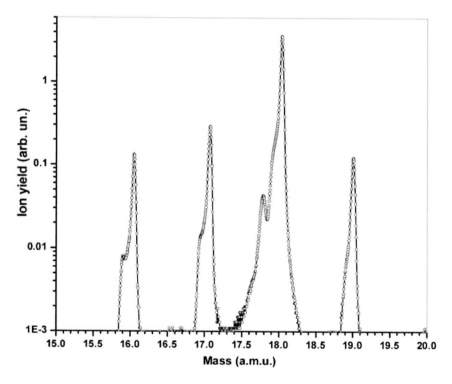

Figure 21. The semi-logarithmic plot of the area of the alanine mass-spectrum within the 15–20 mass range.

The quantitative ratio of the H_2O^+ to NH_4^+ peak intensities at the 60 eV incident electron energy is 11.8:100, i.e., it almost twice exceeds the estimation made in [27] at the 20 eV photon impact. It should be noted that our experiment was carried out within the molecular beam source temperature range that excluded thermal degradation of the initial alanine powder (i.e., within the 150–200°C range). Thus, analyzing fragmentation channels leading to the yield of the ion with the $m/z=18$, ionization of the water vapors released from the alanine sample at elevated temperatures may be excluded.

The results calculated by us prove the fact that H_2O^+ is formed by removing the OH and H fragments with subsequent formation of the C_3H_5NO neutral fragment. The possible pathways of the above positive ion formation could be as follows:

$$C_3H_7NO_2 + e \rightarrow \begin{cases} (OH+H)^+ + C_3H_5NO^- + e; & (84) \\ (OH+H)^+ + C_3H_5NO^0 + 2e; & (85) \\ (OH+H)^+ + C_3H_5NO^+ + 3e; & (86) \end{cases}$$
$$\searrow (H_2O)^+$$

It should be mentioned that we have checked several possibilities of formation of the water molecule. This means that we predicted that the O4, O5 or OH group and different H atoms could be detached under the low-energy impact. However in all cases investigated the calculated appearance energy for the water molecule is higher than that measured by Ipolyi et al. [54] (see Tables 36, 37). Our theoretical analysis and experimental measurements performed at constant temperature prove that this ion could be formed due to joining one H atom and OH or two H atoms and the O atom. On the other hand, the above pathway of the appearance of the molecular water ion from the neutral water molecule could be possible in case of the alanine III molecule, because its stability is lower than that of the alanine I and alanine II molecules. This prediction is based on the analysis of the alanine molecule isomerization. The results of our theoretical investigations indicate that the alanine I molecule may originate from the ground alanine III state due to rotation of the –COOH group. It implies that electron impact may cause isomerization of alanine when the water molecule is formed and ionized.

The ammonium ion NH_4^+ could be formed when the amino acid NH_2 group joins two H atoms from different sides of the initial molecule. As for the hydrogen atom from the hydroxyl group, which is the nearest one to the nitrogen atom, it has been shown experimentally in [27] for the example of the deuterated alanine-*d3* molecule that the NH_4 fragment should be ND_2H_2, i.e., the hydrogen atom from the OH group does not take part in the NH_4 fragment formation. On the other hand, attachment of the H13 atom is less probable for steric reasons.

Table 36. Calculated appearance energies (in eV) for the C_3H_5NO and H_2O fragments produced from the alanine I molecule

H_2O (m=18 a.m.u.) charge	C_3H_5NO (m=71 a.m.u.) charge	Alanine molecule geometry not changed*	Alanine molecule geometry changed**
1	-1	19.39	14.32
1	0	20.39	14.22
1	1	28.68	21.52

*,** – see explanatory notes in Table 2.

Table 37. Calculated appearance energies (in eV) for the C_3H_5NO and H_2O fragments produced from the alanine II molecule

H_2O (m=18 a.m.u.) charge	C_3H_5NO (m=71 a.m.u.) charge	Alanine molecule geometry not changed*	Alanine molecule geometry changed**
1	-1	23.79	15.43
1	0	25.06	16.24
1	1	33.07	24.35

*,** – see explanatory notes in Table 2.

Thus, production of the ammonia ion at dissociative ionization of the α-alanine molecule seems to be possible in case of detachment of three hydrogen atoms from the methyl group via formation of relatively stable 4-term transient states. The results of calculation of the appearance energy of the NH_4^+ fragment for the two alanine molecule isomers are presented in Tables 38 and 39. The ion-pair formation for the above two isomers is the most energetically beneficial process. In this case, location of the atoms of the alanine I, II molecules has almost no influence on the appearance energy for the NH_4^+ ion. However, in case of the neutral complementary fragment formation, the alanine I molecule appears to be the most favorable to produce the ammonium ion.

**Table 38. Calculated appearance energies (in eV) for (NH$_2$ + 2H)
producing the NH$_4$ and C$_3$H$_3$O$_2$ fragments from the alanine I molecule**

NH$_4$ (m=18 a.m.u.) charge	C$_3$H$_3$O$_2$ (m=71 a.m.u.) charge	Alanine molecule geometry not changed*	Alanine molecule geometry changed**
1	-1	24.52	8.46
1	0	24.70	9.69
1	1	34.23	18.51

*,** – see explanatory notes in Table 2.

**Table 39. Calculated appearance energies (in eV) for (NH$_2$ + 2H)
producing the NH$_4$ and C$_3$H$_3$O$_2$ fragments from the alanine II molecule**

NH$_4$ (m=18 a.m.u.) charge	C$_3$H$_3$O$_2$ (m=71 a.m.u.) charge	Alanine molecule geometry not changed*	Alanine molecule geometry changed**
1	-1	23.40	8.45
1	0	25.03	12.94
1	1	33.85	18.88

*,** – see explanatory notes in Table 2.

As seen in the inset in Figure 17, a weak peak related to the doubly charged m/z=43.5 ion is observed. Its atomic composition corresponds to the C$_3$H$_5$NO$_2^{2+}$ ion, i.e., its production proceeds via the detachment of the two hydrogen atoms (most probably, in the form of the H$_2$ molecule) from the initial molecule. Such dissociation channel of the doubly charged alanine molecular ion with singly and multiply charged ion-induced ionization and fragmentation of alanine was not observed experimentally [55]. The authors found that as in the case of single ionization the main fragmentation process after double ionization is scission of the C1–C3 bond. Upon the second ionization, the spatial distribution of the α-alanine cation spin densities shows a substantial charge removed from the COOH group that corresponds to the HOMO-1 and/or HOMO-2 ionization. The CH$_3$ group is only weakly affected by the removal of the second electron. The data on the electron spin density distribution in the doubly charged molecular alanine ion allow one to suggest that elimination of the hydrogen atoms from the hydroxyl and amine groups is the most probable process.

Calculations of the appearance energy for the $C_3H_5NO_2^{2+}$ ion prove that the most energetically probable reaction in this case is:

$$C_3H_7NO_2 + e \rightarrow C_3H_5NO_2^{2+} + (H + H)^- + 2e. \qquad (87)$$

Thus, the hydrogen molecular ion is not formed here.

The analysis of the alanine molecule mass spectrum accompanied by theoretical calculations allowed the main dissociation mechanisms of the above molecule under the low-energy electron impact to be determined. Most of the peaks in the experimental mass spectrum were identified. The appearance energies of the most pronounced ion peaks in the alanine molecule mass-spectrum were measured experimentally and estimated theoretically. For the $C_2H_4N^+$ ion (m=42 a.m.u.), optimization results indicate the changeability of the initial geometrical structure. The mechanism of the structural change CH_3–C–$NH^+ \rightarrow CH_3$–N–CH^+ realized via the intermediate cyclic structure is proposed.

It has been shown that three peaks with m=27, 28 and 29 a.m.u. have double-headed shape, thus, contribution of two ions to each peak was identified. As to the m=28 a.m.u. mass, we may conclude that two isobaric ions peaks in the experimental spectra belong to the $C_2H_4^+$ and CH_2N^+ ions, while at the 70 eV collision energy the channel of the $C_2H_4^+$ ion formation is more efficient than that for the CH_2N^+ ion. The experimentally observed stepwise structure in the ion yield curve for the alanine molecule fragment with the m=28 a.m.u. mass may be due not only to the different pathways of the parent molecule dissociation, but also to the change of the charge of the complementary particles produced and to the conformational isomerism as well.

We have experimentally confirmed the production of the H_2O^+ and NH_4^+ ions formed during the alanine molecule dissociative ionization and established the quantitative ratio of the H_2O^+ to the NH_4^+ peak intensities at the 60 eV incident electron energy.

Despite the fact that the mass spectra show no unambiguous effect due to population of different conformers, the conformational isomerism may influence the near-threshold areas of the ionization and dissociative ionization cross sections. Our calculations show that the presence of intramolecular hydrogen bonds and the differences in the locations of certain atoms in the conformational isomers may lead to the changes in the fragment appearance energies up to 2 eV. Conformational isomerism of the alanine molecule is revealed most distinctly during formation of the ion with the m=18 a.m.u. mass in the case of a zero charge of the complementary fragment.

Thus, variations of the appearance energies for different conformers do exist and sometimes their values lie beyond the experimental error bars. Unfortunately, these peculiarities cannot be resolved in the present experiment.

4.4. Production of Similar Fragments from Different Molecular Targets

The amino acid molecules studied by us in this book, despite their different composition, produce a series of neutral and ionic fragments with the same mass. Therefore, comparison of dynamics of their yield and possible mechanisms of their production is of certain interest when studying the processes of amino acid molecule decomposition. Obviously, it is intriguing to trace their production in this process as well as to study the possible mechanisms of their formation. In this section, we will summarize some results of such studies.

We would like to pay attention that the glycine, alanine and methionine molecules could be presented as the COOH- CHR-NH_2 compounds, where R is -H, -CH_3 or C_2H_4-S-CH_3 in case of glycine, alanine and methionine, respectively. Thist allows one to expect that several fragments with equal mass could be formed under the low-energy electron impact.

Formally, such fragments could be NH_2 (m=16 a.m.u.), CH_2N (m=28 a.m.u.), CH_3N (m=29 a.m.u.), COOH (m=45 a.m.u.), COOHC (m=57 a.m.u.) and COOH–CH–NH_2 (m=74 a.m.u.) and they may be positively or negatively charged or be neutral. It should be emphasized that we have no possibility to measure the mass spectra of negatively charged ions as well as the appearance energy of such fragments, thus, the results presented below are based on the theoretical considerations only.

It is not surprising that the mass spectra of the above amino acids do not reveal the NH_2^+ (m=16 a.m.u.) fragment, because the peaks observed are due to fragmentation of the molecule by preferred cleavage of those bonds, which lead to energetically more favored, i.e., best stabilized, ions. Indeed, NH_2^+ stability is very low as compared to that of the neutral, negatively charged and other positively charged fragments (see Table 40). Hence, the amino fragment could be obtained as the other product when it has negative or zero charge. Our results illustrate the above cases. As an example, when the $C_3H_5^+$ or $C_5H_8OS^+$ fragments appear from the methionine molecule, the (NH_2 + CH_3S + CH_2)^0 or (NH_2 + OH)^0 fragments are formed too. Hence, theoretical investigations prove that, under low-energy electron impact, all the molecules investigated could produce the $m=16$ a.m.u. mass fragment assigned as NH_2^-. This result coincides with that on anionic fragmentation of the above molecules [58, 59].

Table 40. Binding energy per atom (eV) for the differently charged fragments

Binding energy per atom/ fragment	Charge		
	-1	0	1
NH_2	3.43	3.38	0.83
COOH	4.13	4.45	1.31
CH_4N	3.94	4.12	3.06
CH_3N	3.94	4.24	2.63
CH_2N	4.10	4.39	2.27
CHO	4.02	3.63	0.93
CH_6N	4.20	4.32	3.71
$C_4H_{10}NS$	4.24	4.28	3.94
$C_2H_4NO_2$	4.71	4.63	3.82
C_2HO_2	4.78	4.34	2.14
C_3H_7	4.35	4.56	3.90
C_2H_3NO	4.53	4.73	3.60
$C_2H_4NO_2$	4.71	4.63	3.82
C_2H_3NO	3.58	3.71	1.25
$C_4H_{10}NS$	4.25	4.28	3.93

When analyzing the appearance of the fragments with the masses $m=28$ and 29 a.m.u., we would like to draw a special attention to the formation of the fragment with mass $m=30$ a.m.u. due to several reasons: i) this fragment is present in the mass spectra; ii) the fragments with the $m=28$ and 29 a.m.u. masses are related to this fragment.

Obviously, it is interesting to trace their production due to the low-energy electron impact and study the possible mechanisms of their formation. Below we present the analysis of these issues.

Figures 22 and 23 illustrate the threshold areas of the ion yield curves for the CH_2N^+ ($m=28$ a.m.u.) and CH_4N^+ ($m=30$ a.m.u.) ionic fragments resulted from the dissociative ionization of the glycine and methionine molecules.

As seen from Figures 22 and 23, all the curves demonstrate a similar behavior in the initial areas of dissociative ionization functions differing in the curve slopes and absolute values of the ionic fragment appearance potentials.

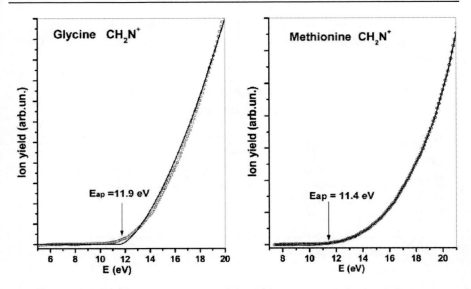

Figure 22. Threshold areas of the CH_2N^+ ion fragment yield from the glycine (left) and methionine (right) molecules. Open circles – experimental data, solid lines – the result of fitting.

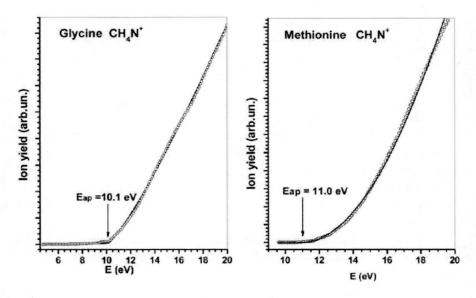

Figure 23. The same as in Figure 22 for the CH_4N^+ ion fragment.

Unfortunately, the lack of the data of other investigations on the appearance energies for the methionine fragments (unlike glycine [27]) does not allow us to make a simple comparative analysis of the fragment production. However, below we present theoretical considerations concerning the appearance energies for both fragments of the initial molecules and our predictions of the possible mechanisms of their production.

The similar peaks in the mass-spectra are due to formation of the parent molecule fragment with the $m=30$ a.m.u. mass. Probable assignments of this peak are the CH_4N^+ and CH_2O^+ ions. As shown above, the first fragment may have two isomeric structures: $NH_2CH_2^+$ and CH_3NH^+. Production of the last fragment (CH_3NH^+) appears to be less probable in view of its thermodynamical instability [26, 27]. As for the CH_2O^+ fragment produced from the glycine or methionine molecule, its appearance requires essential energy, and, therefore, probability of formation of this ion is less than that for the CH_4N^+ ion.

According to our results presented in [46], the appearance energy for the CH_4N^+ fragment from glycine molecule is 10.1 ± 0.1 eV, which is close to the calculated value and the fragment is formed due to the simple rupture of the C-C bond by electron impact.

However in the case of the methionine molecule, formation of the CH_4N^+ ion is more complicated as compared with glycine, because the rearrangement of the one hydrogen atom upon fragmentation is required here. According to our investigations, the fragment with $m=30$ a.m.u. could be produced differently via the pathways (48)–(53) (see above).

The relevant appearance energies are presented in Tables 41 and 42. It is interesting to note that in the above cases the (CH_3N+H) compound becomes the most stable when the H atom is joined with CH_3N^+, i.e., when the equilibrium geometry (the lowest energy geometry) is reached and CH_4N^+ fragment is formed. As mentioned above, in the case of glycine this CH_4N^+ fragment is formed due to a simple bond rupture by electron impact, while in the case of methionine the origin of this fragment is rather complicated: fragmentation process is accompanied by the hydrogen atom attachment to CH_3N^+. The last process is followed by the energy emission (this energy is 6.12 eV when H originates from the C_3H_7S fragment and 7.85 eV when it originates from the COOH fragment).

One may notice that the lowest energy is required to divide the methionine molecule into the ($COO+C_3H_7S$)$^-$ anion and CH_4N^+ cation (see pathway (48)) when the fragments are produced due to the hydrogen atom migration from the hydroxyl group to the carbon atom. It is not surprising that the above energy is higher than that for the glycine molecule, because in the case of the methionine molecule more bonds should be ruptured.

Table 41. Calculated appearance energies (in eV) for the fragments (CH_3N+H) and ($COOH+C_3H_6S$) produced from the neutral methionine molecule

($CH_3N + H$) fragment charge	($COOH + C_3H_6S$) fragment charge	Geometry not changed*	Geometry changed**
1	-1	18.25	6.75
1	0	19.43	8.95
1	1	27.96	16.45

*,** – see explanatory notes in Table 2.

Table 42. Calculated appearance energies (in eV) for the fragments (CH_3N+H) and ($COO+C_3H_7S$) produced from the neutral methionine molecule

($CH_3N + H$) fragment charge	($COO + C_3H_7S$) fragment charge	Geometry not changed*	Geometry changed**
1	-1	17.15	5.86
1	0	20.14	9.08

*,** – see explanatory notes in Table 2.

The fragment peak CH_4N^+ (m=30 a.m.u.) in the glycine, alanine and methionine mass spectra is accompanied by the satellite peaks with m=28 and m=29 a.m.u. The fragment with mass m=29 a.m.u. may be assigned to the COH^+ or CH_3N^+ ion.

According to results of theoretical investigation, it is possible to state that in the case of methionine the COH fragment could not be formed because there is no possibility to form the $C_4H_{10}NS + O$ compound, i.e., the probability of the simultaneous C–O and C–C bonds rupture is very low. Hence, the fragment with m=29 a.m.u. could be CH_3N^+ cation. As mentioned above, this fragment could be formed according to pathways (48)–(51) in the case when this fragment and the H atom are not joined. Despite the fact that the production of the CH_3N fragment takes place at the minimal number of structural changes as compared to the production of the ions with m=30 a.m.u. and m=28 a.m.u., the intensity of the peak with m=29 a.m.u. is very low as compared to that with m=30 a.m.u. or m=28 a.m.u. Such a pattern of the peak intensity distribution is an argument in favor of the hypothesis that the driving force of the molecular ion decay is not the charge localization at the heteroatom (nitrogen in the case of glycine and sulfur in the case of methionine) with further break of the bonds closest to the heteroatom, but the stability of the dissociation products.

Calculations of the binding energy per atom allow the most stable fragment to be predicted, so, in the CH_4N^+, CH_3N^+, CH_2N^+ series, the most stable is CH_4N^+.

The appearance energies for the CH_3N^+ and and $C_2H_4^+$ fragments are presented in Tables 43, 44. Note that the equilibrium geometry of the $(CHO_2+C_3H_7S)$ ionized fragment is not achieved due to the possible self-rupture of C_3H_7S.

Table 43. Calculated appearance energies (in eV) for the CH_3N and $(CHO_2+C_3H_7S)$ fragments of the neutral methionine molecule

CH_3N fragment charge	$(CHO_2 + C_3H_7S)$ fragment charge	Geometry not changed*	Geometry changed**
1	-1	14.20	
1	0	15.49	10.23
1	1	24.03	

*,** – see explanatory notes in Table 2.

Table 44. Calculated appearance energies (in eV) for the C_2H_4 and $(C_2H_4O_2N+ CH_3S)$ fragments of the methionine molecule

C_2H_4 fragment charge	$(C_2H_4O_2N + CH_3S)$ fragment charge	Geometry not changed*	Geometry changed**
1	-1	13.62	9.52
1	0	16.96	10.98
1	1	10.89	2.22

*,** – see explanatory notes in Table 2.

Hence, according to our calculations, the lowest appearance energy of CH_3N^+ is required when the methionine molecule is divided into the ion pair according to the following pathway:

$$C_5H_{11}NO_2S + e \rightarrow CH_3N^+ + (COOH + C_3H_7S)^- + e. \qquad (88)$$

It should be noted that the calculated appearance energy for the CH_3N^+ fragment is higher than that for the $(CH_3N+H)^+$ fragment. Based on these results, we predict that the electron-impact fragmentation of methionine producing the $(CH_3N+H)^+$ fragment is more probable than that for the CH_3N^+ fragment.

For the glycine molecule the formation of the CH_3N^+ fragment occurs with the minimal energy consumption in case of the process $C_2H_5NO_2 + e \rightarrow (CHO_2 + H)^0 + CH_3N^+ + 2e$. Our analysis of the charge distribution for the $(CHO_2 + H)$ fragment group shows that the minimal energies correspond to the production of the CH_2O_2 compound. Thus, the break of the C–C bond accompanied by the H atom migration from the amino group to oxygen of the carbonyl group is the most probable channel of the CH_3N^+ fragment formation.

For all molecules under study the positively charged CH_3N^+ and CH_2N^+ ions could result from the secondary dissociation due to the deprotonation of the CH_4N^+ ions, while the CH_2N^+ ion also appear due to the deprotonation of the CH_3N^+ ion.

In the case of the alanine, the above secondary dissociation is not observed experimentally. In this case, a double-headed peak with the $m=29$ a.m.u. mass is due to the two components and consists of the CHO^+ and CH_3N^+ ions with some preference being given to the CHO^+ ion. The isobaric fragments with the $m=29$ a.m.u. mass could be formed according to the following pathways:

$$C_3H_7NO_2 + e \rightarrow \begin{cases} CHO^+ + C_2H_6NO^0 + 2e; \\ CH_3N^+ + C_2H_4O_2^- + e; \\ CH_3N^+ + C_2H_4O_2^0 + 2e. \end{cases} \qquad (89)$$

It should be noted that our results show that both ions are formed in the collision event. The stability of the CHO^+ fragment is lower than that of the CH_3N^+ ion and this fact explains why the peak with $m=29$ a.m.u. is not assigned as COH^+ in case of glycine and methionine, but this is not clear for the case of alanine.

It is necessary to emphasize that the glycine and methionine molecules mass spectra (see Figures 5, 12) reveal a diffuse peak at about $m^* \sim 26.1$ a.m.u. corresponding to the transition $30 \rightarrow 28$ with the detachment of a neutral fragment with $m=2$ a.m.u., i.e., the secondary fragmentation of the CH_4N^+ ion. Thus, we have observed experimentally that the dehydration proceeds according to pathway $CH_4N^+ \rightarrow (H + H)^0 + CH_2N^+$ produces the molecular hydrogen. Due to this dehydration, when the stable hydrogen molecule is formed as the dissociation product, the fragment with mass $m=29$ is difficult to be produced as well.

There is no doubt that in the case of the glycine molecule the fragment with $m=28$ a.m.u. is the positively charged CH_2N^+ ion because the experiment for the deuterated $d5$- and $d3$-glycine [27] has unambiguously shown that this peak belongs to the CH_2N^+ (CD_2N^+) ion. It is the second intensity-related peak in the glycine molecule mass spectrum. The structure of the CH_2N^+ ion as was mentioned early and shown in Figure7 depends on the bond rupture in the parent or intermediate ion. However, in the case of methionine, the fragment with $m=28$ a.m.u. can be the positively charged CH_2N^+ and $C_2H_4^+$. The stable structure for this $C_2H_4^+$ fragment corresponds to that of the ethylene molecule, and its formation is accompanied by the carbon atom hybridization change from sp^3 to sp^2. However, based on our results of investigations it is not possible to recognize what fragment formation is more probable.

The $C_2H_4^+$ fragment of the methionine molecule could be formed as follows:

$$C_5H_{11}NO_2S + e \rightarrow \begin{cases} C_2H_4^+ + (C_2H_4O_2N + CH_3S)^- + e; & (90) \\[2mm] C_2H_4^+ + (C_2H_4O_2N + CH_3S)^0 + 2e; & (91) \\[2mm] C_2H_4^+ + (C_2H_4O_2N + CH_3S)^+ + 3e. & (92) \end{cases}$$

In this case much attention should be paid to the energy emitted due to the rapid change in the geometrical structure of the C_2H_4 fragment (Figure 24). This energy is equal to 2.44 eV. Hence, if the emitted energy is taken into account, the $C_2H_4^+$ ion is, most probably, produced according to pathway (90).

It is seen that the calculated value 10.98 eV according to pathway (92) corresponding to the equilibrium structure of the fragments agrees well with the measured appearance energy. Thus, CH_3S^+ is also produced giving the peak in the mass spectrum at $m=47$ a.m.u. and the $m=28$ a.m.u. mass fragment could be the $C_2H_4^+$ ion.

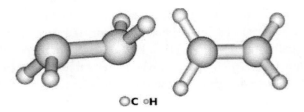

Figure 24. Geometrical structure of the C_2H_4 fragment when it is just formed from the methionine molecule after the bond rupture (left) and that when the equilibrium position is achieved (right).

In case of alanine we conclude that two isobaric ions peaks in the experimental spectra belong to the $C_2H_4^+$ and CH_2N^+ ions, while at the 70 eV collision energy the channel of the $C_2H_4^+$ ion formation is more efficient than that for the CH_2N^+ ion.

In the mass-spectra of the methionine and alanine, the fragment with mass $m=45$ a.m.u. assigned for COOH could be seen as well, however this peak is very small in the glycine molecule mass-spectrum.

Indeed, the fragment with the $m=45$ a.m.u. mass is recognized as CHO_2 in the mass spectra for all molecules and can be formed due to a simple $C-C_\alpha$ bond rupture [60, 61].

In the case of alanine molecule theoretical results prove that reaction

$$C_3H_7NO_2 + e \rightarrow C_2H_6N^+ + CHO_2^- + e \qquad (92)$$

could be more probable due to the stability of the fragments produced, however the comparison of the calculated and measured appearance energies indicates that reaction

$$C_3H_7NO_2 + e \rightarrow C_2H_6N^+ + CHO_2^0 + 2e \qquad (93)$$

is more energetically probable, i.e., $C_2H_6N^+$ and CHO_2^0 formation is more expected, while the CHO_2^+ could be formed only in the case when the hydrogen bond $O\cdots H$ in the alanine molecule occurs favoring this fragment stability (see Table 40). Hence, from the stability of the $C_2H_6N^+$ and CHO_2^+ ions comparison as well as from the condition necessary for these fragments formation, it becomes obvious, why the intensity of the $m=44$ a.m.u. peak in the mass spectra of alanine is larger than that of the $m=45$ a.m.u. peak, but there are no enough data to explain, why the neutral COOH fragment is produced instead of more stable negatively charged one.

It is interesting that in the case of methionine the fragment with the $m=45$ a.m.u. mass is also complementary to the $C_4H_{10}NS$ ($m=104$ a.m.u.) one. We found that the CHO_2^+ fragment could be formed according to the following pathway:

$$C_5H_{11}NO_2S + e \rightarrow CHO_2^+ + C_4H_{10}NS^0 + 2e, \qquad (94)$$

but this way is less probable than the channel of the $C_4H_{10}NS^+$ fragment formation:

$$C_5H_{11}NO_2S + e \rightarrow CHO_2^- + C_4H_{10}NS^+ + e. \qquad (95)$$

The last conclusion is made based on the results obtained:
- the stability of the $C_4H_{10}NS^+$ and $C_4H_{10}NS^0$ fragments is almost equal;
- the stability of the CHO_2^- fragment is higher than that of the CHO_2^+ one.

It is necessary to mention that one electron shift from the ionized nitrogen atom and carbon atom results in formation of a double bond accompanied by the energy release when $C_4H_{10}NS^+$ is formed. This observation allows us to predict that formation of the positively charged $COOH^+$ fragment could be interpreted as a casual case.

In the case of glycine, to form the COOH (CHO_2) fragment, the C-C bond must be broken and the CH_4N ($m=30$ a.m.u.) fragment appears. Calculated binding energy per atom shows that CH_4N^+ is three times stable than $COOH^+$ (see Table 40). Hence, formation of CH_4N^+ ($m=30$ a.m.u.) and $COOH^-$ ($m=45$ a.m.u.) is more probable because of the energetically more favored ion formation, and this leads to the absence of the peak at $m=45$ a.m.u. in the glycine mass spectrum.

Summarizing all the results discussed above, one may predict that the COOH fragment is formed when the alanine, glycine or methionine molecules undergo low-energy electron impact, but the charge of the fragment could be negative or zero.

The peaks at $m=44$ a.m.u. and $m=42$ a.m.u. are observed in the experimental mass spectra of alanine and methionine quite unexpectedly. It is interesting that in both molecules the peak at $m=44$ a.m.u. could be attributed to the formation of the $C_2H_6N^+$ fragment, the appearance of which is described above for the case of alanine. However, we failed to find the channel of this fragment formation from the methionine molecule: the calculated energy of this fragment appearance is approximately 5 eV less than the measured one or 4 eV higher, when this peak is assigned as CS. In the case of methionine, to form the $C_2H_6N^+$ fragment at least two C–C bonds should be broken and one H atom could joint the parent C_2H_5N fragment.

In the mass range of 40–50 a.m.u., a very small peak at $m=42$ a.m.u. was observed experimentally in the methionine and alanine mass spectra. This peak may be attributed to the $C_2H_4N^+$ ion. In case of the alanine molecule, this peak may be assigned to the CH_3CHN^+, $NH_2CH_2C^+$ and CH_3CNH^+ ions, respectively. Comparison of the values of binding energy per atom indicates that the CH_3CNH^+ fragment is the most stable, however formation of this fragment from alanine requires migration of at least two H atoms (Table 45). On the other hand, based on our results obtained, formation of CH_3CHN^+ is energetically more probable, because in this case the weaker C–C, N–H and N–H bonds could be broken. It implies that the mechanism of the $C_2H_4N^+$ ion production includes detachment of a carboxyl group from the initial molecule accompanied by the molecular hydrogen formation as well as the H atoms migration.

Table 45. Total (internal) energies of the $C_2H_4N^+$ fragment with different geometrical structure

Fragment structure	Total energy, a.u.	Total energy difference, eV
NH_2-CH_2-C	-132.88	2.84
CH_3-CH-N	-132.97	0.54
CH_3-C-NH	-132.99	0
CH_2-CH-NH	-132.91	2.15
CH_2-C-NH_2	-132.97	0.44

In case of the methionine molecule, this fragment could be formed via the following pathway:

$$C_5H_{11}NO_2 S + e \rightarrow C_2H_4N^+ + (C_2H_5S + H + CHO_2)^- + e, \qquad (96)$$

where the $C_2H_4N^+$ ion has the following structure: CH_2CHNH. Formation of this structure was predicted based on the investigation of the bond order. On the other hand, we have checked the channel of formation of the fragment with the CH_2-C-NH_2 structure that is more stable than CH_2-CH-NH, but less stable than $CH_3C=NH^+$. It should be mentioned that the measured appearance energy for this fragment is 12.9 eV, while calculated one is 9.37 eV or 6.95 eV.

Taking into account that the fragments are not the most stable ones, we may predict migration of H that requires the energy of 2.15 eV or 0.44 eV. Hence, the appearance of the $m=42$ a.m.u. ion in the case of the alanine and methionine molecules is different only in the structure of the initial $C_2H_4N^+$ ion.

To indicate the stabilities of structures under study the energy difference is presented as well, when the lowest energy is assumed to be zero.

In the case of glycine, formation of the $C_2H_4N^+$ fragment ($m=42$ a.m.u.) the C=O and the C–OH bonds must be broken. It is known, that the average bond enthalpy (i.e., the energy required to break a chemical bond) for the C=O and the C–O bonds is ~8.28 eV and ~3.7 eV respectively, while for C–C it is about 3.61eV [62]. The simplest observation allows one to predict that reaction producing the $C_2H_4N^+$ ($m=42$ a.m.u.) fragment is energy consuming and, thus, should be deemed not possible or having very low probability to occur.

We also predicted formation of the COOHC ($m=57$ a.m.u.) fragment and the relevant peak is present only in the methionine mass-spectrum though its intensity is not high. However, this peak is assigned as $C_3H_7N^+$ and the observation is explained taking into account that the peaks in the spectra are due to the molecule fragmentation by preferred cleavage of those bonds, which produce the most stabilized positive ion, i.e., $C_3H_7N^+$ is more stable than COOHC (C_2HO_2) (Table 40). Thus, it could be the reason why the spectra of alanine and glycine show no peak at $m=57$ a.m.u. assigned to COOHC: stability of the positive-ion is lower than that of the other fragments formed due to fragmentation of the molecules described. However, theoretical results prove, that in the case of alanine $C_2H_3NOH^+$ ($m=57$ a.m.u.) could form by following channel:

$$C_3H_7NO_2 + e \rightarrow C_2H_3NO^+ + (CH_3 + O + H)^0 + 2e, \qquad (97)$$

because the stability of the fragment $C_2H_3NO^+$ is higher and, as consequence, the appearance energy (11.23 eV) is about 6 eV less than that of the C_2HO_2 fragment. Moreover, stability of this $C_2H_3NO^+$ fragment is higher than that of other fragments formed via pathway (97).

Similar situation could take place in the case of glycine, because the theoretical investigation exhibited the most energetically probable channel:

$$C_2H_5NO_2 + e \rightarrow C_2H_3NO^+ + (H + O + H)^0 + 2\,e \rightarrow C_2H_3NO^+ + H_2O^0 + 2e, \qquad (98)$$

when the $C_2H_3NOH^+$ fragment and the neutral water molecule are formed. The calculated appearance energy for this fragment is 9.38 eV that is less than that for other reactions. Hence, this fragment peak is difficult to be measured experimentally.

Our predicted $C_2H_3NO_2$ (m=73 a.m.u.) and $C_2H_4NO_2$ (m=74 a.m.u.) fragments are not observed in the mass spectra of the molecules under study. In the case of glycine the fragment m=74 a.m.u., is probably, negatively charged because of the deprotonation of the molecule, while in the case of the alanine and methionine molecules this fragment could be formed due to removing the R group. Our theoretical data prove the most probable channels of the m=74 a.m.u. fragment formation:

$$C_3H_7NO_2 + e \rightarrow C_2H_4NO_2^+ + CH_3^0 + 2e \text{ (10.33 eV appearance energy)}$$

$$C_5H_{11}NO_2S + e \rightarrow C_2H_4NO_2^+ + C_3H_7S^0 + 2e \text{ (9.79 eV appearance energy)}.$$

Relatively small appearance energy as well as high stability of the fragment (Table 40) confirm prediction that the relevant peak may be present in the mass spectra of both molecules. The reason of the absence of the peak at m=74 a.m.u. in the spectra measured could be the chemical stability of this fragment

Hence, we have shown that the different substitutents influence fragmentation of the amino acid molecules, i.e., only few amino acids produce the same fragments despite their core part similarities. The observations of that kind could be of great importance for studying the malignant transformations in living cells under the influence of ionizing radiation and also provide useful radiation therapy effect on tumors in human beings.

CONCLUSION

We have studied both experimentally and theoretically the mass spectra of the amino acid molecules (glycine, methionine and alanine) and have identified their main components related both to the parent molecular ions and their ionic fragments yield. The ionization energies of the initial molecules and the appearance potentials of their main fragments have been measured. The analysis of the obtained results using the newly developed DFT approach has allowed the principal mechanisms of the initial amino acid molecules dissociation/fragmentation to be established with the allowance made for the charges of the ionic fragments produced. This will help one to expand the conventional mass-spectrometric analysis that takes into account the positively charged ions only and assumes that the complementary dissociation products are neutral.

It has been found for the glycine molecule that the appearance of its main fragment, the CH_4N^+ ion, has a stepwise character and is related not only to ionization from different molecular orbitals of the parent molecule but also to the charge change in the complementary fragment.

The yield of the doubly charged glycine molecule ionic fragment CH_2NHCO^{2+} has been found allowing the assumption to be made that the mechanism of its production is due to the simultaneous loss of two electrons and detachment of the water molecule.

It has been found that in case of dissociative ionization of the methionine molecule the dissociation of the skeleton C3–S, C5–C6 and C4–C5 bonds takes place being accompanied by the HOMO orbital ionization with the n-electron elimination. The main channel of this process corresponds to the β-bond rupture with respect to the sulfur atom.

In the alanine molecule, the conformational isomerism has been revealed at the $m=18$ a.m.u. ion formation in case of a zero charge of the complementary fragment.

It has been shown that different substitutents influence greatly the process of the amino acid molecules fragmentation, i.e., only few amino acids produce the same fragments despite their core part similarities. Such observations could be very important in studying the malignant transformations in living cells under the influence of ionizing radiation also providing useful radiation therapy effect on tumors in human beings.

ACKNOWLEDGMENTS

The authors would like to thank Prof. M. Cegla from Jagellonian University, Krakow, Poland, and our colleagues Prof. A. Imre (Institute of Electron Physics) and V. Patasiene (Vilnius University) for their technical support and assistance in carrying out these studies. Special thanks go to the InSpire and NGI.LT projects for the resources and support of theoretical calculations provided as well as to the COST MP0802 activity.

REFERENCES

[1] U. Meierhenrich, *Amino acids and the asymmetry of life*, Berlin: Springer Verlag. (2008).

[2] L. Delaye and A. Lazcano, *Physics of Life Reviews,* 2 47 (2005).

[3] F. Rogalewicz, Y. Hoppilliard and G. Ohanessian, *Int. J. Mass Spectr.* 195/196 565 (2000).

[4] S. Cristoni and L.R. Bernardi, *Mass. Spectr. Rev.* 22 369 (2003).

[5] B.D. Michael and P.A. O'Neill, *Science* 287 1603 (2000).

[6] S. Denifl, B. Sonnweber, G. Hanel, P. Scheier and T.D. Märk, *Int. J. Mass Spectr.* 238 47 (2004).

[7] A. Brack, *The Molecular Origins of Life,* Cambridge University Press, Cambridge (1998).

[8] National Institute of Standards, Standard Reference Database: Chemistry Webbook – http://webbook.nist gov.

[9] MI 1201 Mass Spectrometer. Instruction Manual, SELMI Corporation, (2002).

[10] E. I. Selifonova, R. K. Chernova and O. E. Koblova, *Izvestia Saratov. Univer. Ser. Chem. Biol. Ecol.* 8 23 (2008).

[11] G. Hanel, B. Gstir, T. Fiegele, F. Hagelberg, K. Becker, P. Scheier, A. Snegursky and T. D. Märk, *J. Chem. Phys.* 116 2456 (2002).

[12] A. N. Zavilopulo and A. V. Snegursky, *Techn. Phys. Lett.* 28 913 (2002).

[13] R. S. Freund, R. C. Wetzel, R. J. Shul and T. R. Hayes, *Phys. Rev. A.* 41 3575 (1990).

[14] A. D. Becke, *J. Chem. Phys.* 98 5648 (1993).

[15] R. A. Kendall, T. H. Dunning Jr and R. J. J. Harrison, *Chem. Phys.* 96 6796 (1992).

[16] P. McWeeny and B. T. Sucliffe, *Methods of Molecular Quantum Mechanics*, Moscow, (1972).

[17] R. Zahradnik and R. Polac, *Zaklady kvantove chemie*, Moscow, (1979).

[18] J. B. Collins, P. R. Schleyer, J. S. Binkley and J. A. Pople, *J. Chem. Phys.* 64 12 (1976).

[19] T. H. Dunning Jr., *J. Chem. Phys.* 90 1007 (1989).

[20] R. C. Raffenetti, *J. Chem. Phys.* 58 4452 (1973).

[21] R. G. Par and W. Yang, *Density-functional theory of atoms and molecules*, Oxford Univ. Press, Oxford, (1989).

[22] *Density-Functional Methods in Chemistry and Materials Science*, (ed. M. Springborg), John Wiley & Sons, Chichester, New York, Weinheim, Brisbane, Singapore, Toronto, (1997).

[23] J. Kalade, V. Mickevicius and D. Grabauskas, *Thermodynamical and Statistical Physics*, Vilnius, Mokslas, (1982).

[24] C. Lee, W. Yang and R. G. Parr, *Phys. Rev. B* 37 785 (1988).

[25] A. V. Snegursky, F. F. Chipev, A. N. Zavilopulo and O. B. Shpenik, *Radiat. Phys. Chem.* 76 604 (2007).

[26] V. S. Vukstich, A. I. Imre, L. G. Romanova and A. V. Snegursky, *J. Phys. B.* 43 185208 (2010).

[27] H-W. Jochims, M. Schwell, J-L. Chotin, M. Clembino, F. Dulieu, H. Baumgärtel and S. Leach, *Chem. Phys.* 298 279 (2004).

[28] R. A. J. O'Hair, S. Blanksby, M. Styles and J.H. Bowie, *Int. Journ. Mass Spectrom.* 182/183 203 (1999).

[29] G. A. Junk and H. J. Svec, *J. Am. Chem. Soc.* 85 839 (1963).

[30] L. F. Pacios P. C. Gómez, *J. Mol. Struct. (Teochem).* 544 237 (2001).

[31] M. Schwell, H.-W. Jochims, H. Baumgartel, F. Dulieu and S. Leach, *Planet. Space Sci.* 54 1073 (2006).

[32] R. Maul, M. Preuss, F. Ortmann, K. Hannewald, and F. Bechstedt, *J. Phys. Chem. A*, 111 4370 (2007).

[33] A. F. Lago, L. H. Coutinho, R. R. T. Marinho, A. Naves de Brito and G. G. B. de Souza, *Chem. Phys.* 307 9 (2004).

[34] D. Shemesh, G. M. Chaban, and R. B. Gerber, *J. Phys. Chem. A.* 108 11477 (2004).

[35] D. Shemesh and R. B. Gerber, *J. Chem. Phys.* 122 241104 (2005).

[36] A. T. Lebedev, *Mass-Spectrometry in Organic Chemistry*, BINOM, Moscow (2003).

[37] U. Salzner and R. J. Baer, *Chem. Phys.* 131 231101 (2009).

[38] O. Plekan, V. Feyer, R. Richter, M. Coreno, M. Simone, K. C. Prince and V. Carravetta, *J. Phys. Chem. A* 111 10998 (2007).

[39] L. S. Cederbaum, *J. Phys. B.* 8 290 (1975).

[40] D. Dehareng and G. Dive, *Int. J. Mol. Sci.* 5 301 (2004).

[41] H. Jürgen, *Gross Mass Spectrometry. A Textbook.* 2nd Edition. Springer-Verlag, Berlin-Heidelberg (2011).

[42] O. Plekan, V. Feyer, R. Richter, M. Coreno, M. de Simone and K. C. Prince. *Chem. Phys.* 334 53 (2007).

[43] V. V. Afrosimov, A. A. Basalaev, E. A. Berezovskaya, M. N. Panov, O. V. Smirnov and A. V. Tulub, *Techn. Phys.* 51 1553 (2006).

[44] R. Johnstone, *Mass-Spectrometry for Organic Chemists.* Cambridge University Press, Cambridge (1972).

[45] R. S. Mulliken, *J. Chem. Phys.* 23 1833 (1955).

[46] J. Tamuliene, L. G. Romanova, V. S. Vukstich and A. V. Snegursky, *Nucl. Instr. Meth. B.* 279 128 (2012).

[47] K. Biemann, J. Seibl and F. J. Gapp, *J. Am. Chem. Soc.* 89 2719 (1967).

[48] J. Tamuliene, L. G. Romanova, V. S. Vukstich and A. V. Snegursky, *Chem. Phys.* 404 74 (2012).

[49] K. V. Rajesh, C. Majumder, O. D. Jayakumar, S. K. Kulshreshtaha and J. P. Mittal, *Proc. Indian Acad. Sci. (Chem. Sci.)* 113 129 (2001).

[50] H. M. Jaeger, H. F. Schaefer III, J. Demaison, A. G. Csaszár and W. D. Allen, *J. Chem. Theory Comput.* 6 3066 (2010).

[51] S. Blanco, A. Lesarri, J. C. Lopez, and J. L. Alonso, *J. Am. Chem. Soc.* 126 11675 (2004).

[52] Yongjun Hu and E. R. Bernstein, *J. Chem. Phys.* 128 164311–164321 (2008).

[53] S. Simon, A. Gilb, M. Sodupeb, and J. Bertran, *J. Mol. Struct.: Theochem,* 727 191 (2005).

[54] Ipolyi, P. Cicman, S. Denifl, V. Matejcik, P. Mach, J. Urban, P. Scheier, T. D. Märk and S. Matejcik, *Int. J. Mass. Spectr.* 252 228 (2006).

[55] S. Bari, P. Sobocinski, J. Postma, F. Alvarado, R. Hoekstra, V. Bernigaud, B. Manil, J. Rangama, B. Huber and T. Schlathölter, *J. Chem. Phys.* 128 074306 (2008).

[56] A. F. Lago, L. H. Coutinho, R. R. T. Marinho, A. Naves de Brito and G. G. B. de Souza, *Chem. Phys.* 307 9 (2004).

[57] J. Tamuliene, L. G. Romanova, V. S. Vukstich and A. V. Snegursky, *Chem. Phys.* 404 36 (2012).

[58] F. Ferreira da Silva, M. Lan, D. Almeide, G. Garc and P. Lim-o-Veira, *Eur. Phys. J.* 66 78 (2012).

[59] B. J. Figard, *Electron-Molecule Interactions of Amino Acids and Peptides,* Ph.D. Thesis, Oregon State University, (2007).

[60] A. V. Snegursky, J. Tamuliene, V. S. Vukstich and L. G. Romanova, Methionine Molecule Electron-Impact-Induced Fragmentation: Mechanisms and Chemical Structure. In: *Methionine: Biosynthesis, Chemical Structure and Toxicity,* (Ed. A.V. Snegursky), Nova Science, New York (2013).

[61] J. Tamuliene, L. G. Romanova, V. S. Vukstich and A. V. Snegursky, *Lith. J. Phys.* 53 195 (2013).

[62] Mr. Kent's Chemistry Page: Bond Enthalpy – http: //www.kent chemistry.com.

INDEX

N

O

P

Q

R

S